Forest Trees of Illinois

TENTH EDITION

2009 update by University of Illinois Extension
Jay C. Hayek, Editor

Original text by Robert H. Mohlenbrock
Department of Botany, Southern Illinois University

TABLE OF CONTENTS

Acknowledgements 4

Introduction 4

Illustrated Glossary 7

Key to the Trees of Illinois in Spring, Summer, and Autumn 10

Key to the Trees of Illinois in Winter 28

Trees of Illinois: Species Descriptions and Illustrations 41

Botanical Terminology 327

Additional Resources

Illinois Department of Natural Resources 329

The Morton Arboretum 329

University of Illinois at Urbana-Champaign, Department of
    Natural Resources and Environmental Sciences 330

University of Illinois Arboretum 330

University of Illinois Extension Forestry 331

Southern Illinois University–Carbondale 331

Shawnee National Forest 332

Illinois Forestry Development Council 332

State Tree of Illinois 332

Illinois Big Tree Register 333

Illinois Forestry Association 333

Illinois Tree Farm 333

The Illinois Steward Magazine 334

Index to Common and Scientific Names 335

Illustration Credits 339

Acknowledgements

The editor and the publishing staff at Information Technology and Communication Services in the College of Agricultural, Consumer and Environmental Sciences at the University of Illinois, Urbana-Champaign, and University of Illinois Extension would like to acknowledge and thank the Illinois Department of Natural Resources for allowing us to publish this tenth edition.

The editor also wishes to thank and acknowledge the United States Department of Agriculture, Cooperative State Research, Education, and Extension Service for financial assistance (Renewable Resources Extension Act) in the production of this edition.

Introduction

As a professional forester and as an admirer of forestry and all trees small and large, it is my great pleasure to welcome you to the tenth edition of *Forest Trees of Illinois.* The first edition was published in 1927 by Wilbur R. Mattoon and R. B. Miller, two prominent Illinois foresters of that era. In 1955, Dr. George D. Fuller of the Illinois State Museum and E. E. Nuuttila, state forester of Illinois, revised the book. Subsequently in 1973, Dr. Robert H. Mohlenbrock of Southern Illinois University–Carbondale reworked the publication with new text, bark images, updated species-distribution maps, and illustrations. *Forest Trees of Illinois* has become an iconic publication used by Illinois foresters, biologists, botanists, teachers, students, and aspiring naturalists for more than 80 years.

Helpful revisions, including the addition of a glossary of botanical terms, were made throughout this edition where appropriate to the benefit of the reader. The majority of the bark pictures have been updated to higher-resolution photographs to provide the readers with images that depict more typical bark characteristics. Including the changes made in the ninth edition, the editor has added a total of four new native tree species: balsam poplar *(Populus balsamifera)*, nuttall oak *(Quercus texana)*, northern white-cedar *(Thuja occidentalis)*, and yellow buckeye *(Aesculus flava).* We believe the revisions and updated photography greatly enhance the quality and value of this popular and affordable publication.

Almost every kind of plant in the world is known by a common name and a scientific or botanical name. The common name is the name used locally by residents of an area, but it is often of limited value because people in different areas may have different names for the same plant. The scientific name—composed of two words, the genus name (which is always capitalized and italicized, and the specific epithet, which is italicized but not capitalized)—is the same the world over (for example, *Quercus alba;* "*Quercus*" is the genus name and "*alba*" is the specific epithet).

Owners and readers of previous editions of this publication may immediately notice some content changes, especially changes made to common tree names. Because common tree names are often used with great inconsistency (for example, yellow-poplar, tulip-poplar, tuliptree; and American hornbeam, musclewood, blue-beech), the editor has adopted the preferred common names for individual tree species, with several minor exceptions, based on Little's 1979 *Checklist of United States Trees (Native and Naturalized)*. Moreover, botanical nomenclature, just like trees, tends to change and even revert over time, that is, *Carya tomentosa* (mockernut hickory) is now classified taxonomically as *Carya alba*. Nomenclature used throughout this edition is current as of August 2008 and follows *Integrated Taxonomic Information System's* online database (www.itis.gov).

Forests of Illinois

Despite the "Prairie State" nickname, Illinois is home to 4.8 million acres of forest land, covering over 13% of the state. The vast majority of our native forests are high-quality hardwood stands composed of mixed oak, hickory, black walnut, black cherry, ash, elm, hackberry, sycamore, cottonwood, maple, beech, basswood, and yellow-poplar. In addition, scattered stands of native and planted conifers—such as tamarack, eastern white pine, red pine, jack pine, loblolly pine, shortleaf pine, eastern redcedar, and baldcypress—dot the state from north to south. Illinois's predominant forest-cover types include oak–hickory, elm–ash–sycamore, maple–beech–basswood, mixed pine, and oak–gum–cypress. According to data from the Illinois Natural History Survey, over 180 native trees and shrubs are found throughout the state.

Illinois, during and after settlement, has always been dependent on its forests and trees for economic viability and environmental stability, from sawmills to furniture and pallet manufacturing; from the multitude of ecosystem services forests provide (including clean air, soil and water quality, wildlife habitat, carbon sequestration, and aesthetics) to the spiritual pleasures of hiking through a mature stand of stately oak trees. In addition, let's not forgot the significant economic impact—over $1.3 billion annually to the state's economy—forests play in regard to statewide hunting, water quality for fishing, wildlife viewing, and outdoor recreation. And of course, it is extremely difficult to overlook the huge economic impact the forest-products sector plays in Illinois: forest-based employment exceeds 68,000 workers in Illinois and contributes nearly $30 billion in annual sales volume to Illinois's economy. It should therefore come as no surprise that additional education and outreach, financial incentives, and technical resources are necessary to manage, conserve, and expand this invaluable forest resource.

Species Distribution Maps

A map is provided for the believed distribution of each species listed in this publication. Shaded areas represent a specimen of a wild tree recorded and collected in that county. A "wild" tree is defined as growing without cultivation; it excludes planted ornamentals and tree plantations. However, these distribution maps should be used only as a general guide and do not necessarily represent the absolute natural distribution of that particular species throughout the state. Outlier populations, unidentified specimens, misidentified specimens, and incomplete data unfortunately result in inherent limitations to these distribution maps. Please note that distribution maps of nonnative, naturalized species are rather subjective and should not be interpreted as absolute.

Keys to Forest Trees of Illinois

A key is a botanical device that enables the reader, through proper selection of a series of choices, to identify a specimen at hand. Separate keys are provided for trees during the spring, summer, autumn, and winter seasons. Begin at the first pair of number 1s, choose the statement that best fits the unknown specimen, and then go to the next pair of statements beneath. Continue this same procedure until you are confident the identity of the plant has been discerned.

Illustrated Glossary and Botanical Terms

To differentiate one kind of tree from another, it is necessary to learn the key distinguishing characteristics of individual species. Basic botanical terminology and commonly encountered characteristics of leaves, twigs, and fruits are illustrated and briefly described on the following pages. A thorough understanding of morphological characteristics and botanical terminology can ensure quicker and more accurate tree identification.

Illustrated Glossary

Leaf Forms and Arrangement

SIMPLE

OPPOSITE

PINNATELY COMPOUND

ALTERNATE

PALMATELY COMOUND

WHORLED

BIPINNATELY COMPOUND

LEAF SHAPES

LANCEOLATE

OBLANCEOLATE

OBLONG

ELLIPTICAL

OVATE

OBOVATE

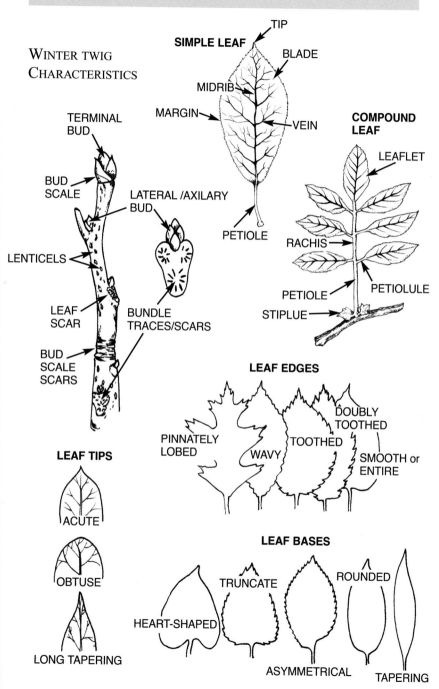

WINTER TWIG CHARACTERISTICS

TERMINAL BUD

BUD SCALE

LATERAL /AXILARY BUD

LENTICELS

LEAF SCAR

BUNDLE TRACES/SCARS

BUD SCALE SCARS

SIMPLE LEAF

TIP

BLADE

MIDRIB

MARGIN

VEIN

PETIOLE

COMPOUND LEAF

LEAFLET

RACHIS

PETIOLULE

PETIOLE

STIPLUE

LEAF EDGES

PINNATELY LOBED

WAVY

TOOTHED

DOUBLY TOOTHED

SMOOTH or ENTIRE

LEAF TIPS

ACUTE

OBTUSE

LONG TAPERING

LEAF BASES

HEART-SHAPED

TRUNCATE

ROUNDED

ASYMMETRICAL

TAPERING

Fruit

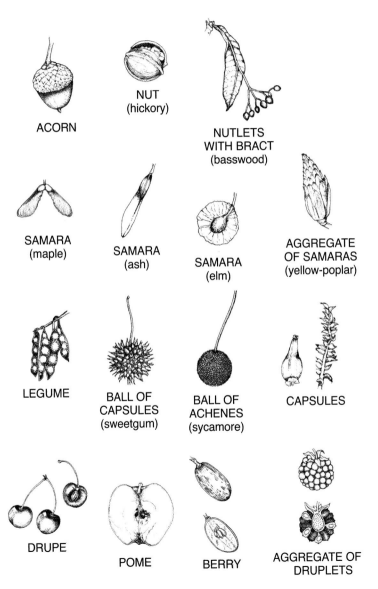

ACORN

NUT
(hickory)

NUTLETS
WITH BRACT
(basswood)

SAMARA
(maple)

SAMARA
(ash)

SAMARA
(elm)

AGGREGATE
OF SAMARAS
(yellow-poplar)

LEGUME

BALL OF
CAPSULES
(sweetgum)

BALL OF
ACHENES
(sycamore)

CAPSULES

DRUPE

POME

BERRY

AGGREGATE OF
DRUPLETS

Key to the Trees of Illinois in Spring, Summer, and Autumn

1. Leaves needlelike or scalelike ....Group A
1. Leaves broad and flat, never needlelike or scalelike
  2. Leaves compound (divided into 3 or more leaflets) ....Group B
  2. Leaves simple
    3. Leaves opposite or whorled ....Group C
    3. Leaves alternate
      4. Leaves neither toothed nor lobed ....Group D
      4. Leaves toothed, or lobed, or both
        5. Leaves toothed, but not lobed ....Group E
        5. Leaves lobed ....Group F

GROUP A

Leaves needlelike or scalelike, often evergreen
1. Needles in clusters of 2 or more
   2. Needles in clusters of 10 or more, falling off during autumn
      3. Needles blue–green; cone-scales smooth . . . .*Larix laricina*
      3. Needles bright green; cone-scales hairy . . . .*Larix decidua*
   2. Needles in clusters of 2–5, evergreen
      4. Needles in clusters of 5 . . . .*Pinus strobus*
      4. Needles in clusters of 2–3
         5. Needles in clusters of 2
            6. Most or all the needles less than 3 inches long, usually twisted
               7. Needles up to $1^{1}/_{2}$ inches long; sheath at base of leaves not longer than $^{1}/_{8}$ inch . . . .*Pinus banksiana*
               7. Needles 2–3 inches long; sheath at base of needles at least $^{1}/_{3}$ inch long . . . .*Pinus sylvestris*
            6. Most or all the needles longer than 3 inches, rarely twisted
               8. Needles mostly less than 5 inches long; cone-scale with a small spine . . . .*Pinus echinata*
               8. Needles mostly more than 5 inches long; cone-scale without a spine . . . .*Pinus resinosa*
         5. Needles in clusters of 3, sometimes 2
            9. Needles flexible, mostly less than 5 inches long; sheath at base of needles about $^{1}/_{4}$ inch long . . . .*Pinus echinata*
            9. Needles stiff, mostly more than 5 inches long; sheath at base of needles about 1 inch long . . . .*Pinus taeda*
1. Leaves solitary
   10. Leaves deciduous
      11. Leaves flat, two-ranked, feathery, and deciduous . . .*Taxodium distichum*
         12. Leaves persistent
            13. Leaves persistent, of 2 types, some scalelike and about $^{1}/_{8}$ inch long, some needlelike up to $^{1}/_{3}$ inch long, cone fleshy . . . .*Juniperous virginiana*
            13. Leaves persistent, scalelike, fragrant; cone small and woody . . . .*Thuja occidentalis*

GROUP B

Compound leaves broad and flat, never needlelike or scalelike
1. Leaves alternate
  2. Leaflets 3 . . . .*Ptelea trifoliata*
  2. Leaflets 5 or more
    3. Rachis winged on either side . . . .*Rhus copallina*
    3. Rachis not winged
      4. Leaves with an even number of leaflets, often bipinnately compound
        5. Leaflets not more than $1/2$ inch wide
          6. Legumes usually 12 inches long or longer, with 6 or more seeds
          . . . .*Gleditsia triacanthos*
          6. Legumes 1–2 inches long, with 1–3 seeds . . . . . .*Gleditsia aquatica*
        5. Some or all the leaflets at least 1 inch wide
          7. Leaves bipinnately compound; leaflets smooth along the edges;
          leaves without a foul odor when crushed . . . . .*Gymnocladus dioicus*
          7. Leaves pinnately compound; leaflets usually with a few coarse teeth
          along the edges; leaves with a foul odor when crushed
          . . . .*Ailanthus altissima*
      4. Leaves with odd number of leaflets, pinnately compound
      (bipinnately compound in *Aralia spinosa,* rachis has scattered prickles)
        8. Leaflets without teeth along the edges
          9. Leaflets less than 1 inch broad and 2 inches long; twigs with
          short spines at base of petioles . . . .*Robinia pseudoacacia*
          9. Leaflets up to 4 inches long and up to 2 inches wide; twigs
          without spines
            10.   Some or all the leaflets alternate; base of petiole
            conspicuously swollen . . . .*Cladrastis kentukea*
            10.   All the leaflets opposite; base of petiole not swollen
            . . . .*Toxicodendron vernix*
        8. Leaflets toothed along the edges
          11.   Leaves binnately compound, often with small prickles on the
          rachis . . . .*Aralia spinosa*
          11.   Leaves pinnately compound, rachis without prickles
            12.   All leaves with 11 or more leaflets
              13.   Rachis and undersurface of leaves completely smooth . . .
              . . . .*Rhus glabra*
              13.   Rachis and undersurface of leaves (at least on the
              veins) hairy

14. Pith of twigs chambered when cut lengthwise
   15. Pith pale brown; bark dark brown, with roughened ridges . . . . *Juglans nigra*
   15. Pith dark brown; bark gray, with smooth ridges. . . . . *Juglans cinerea*
14. Pith of twigs solid
   16. Leaves strongly aromatic when crushed; twigs not covered with velvety hairs
      17. Bud scales with yellow hairs; nut $1^1/2$ to 2 times longer than wide . . .*Carya illinoinensis*
      17. Bud scales without yellow hairs; nut about as wide as long . . . .*Carya aquatica*
   16. Leaves not aromatic when crushed; twigs covered with velvety hairs . . . .*Rhus hirta*
12. Some or all leaves with fewer than 11 leaflets
   18. Buds with 4–6 scales arranged in pairs; most of the leaves with at least 9 leaflets
      19. Terminal leaflet without a petiolule or with a very short petiolule; buds mustard yellow . . . . .*Carya cordiformis*
      19. Terminal leaflet with a well-developed petiolule; buds reddish brown . . . .*Carya aquatica*
   18. Buds with 6 or more overlapping scales; most of the leaves with fewer than 9 leaflets (except sometimes in *Carya alba* and *C. laciniosa*), never with 11 leaflets
      20. Teeth along the leaf margin with small tufts of hair . . . .*Carya ovata*
      20. Teeth along the leaf margin without small tufts of hair
         21. Undersurface of leaflets densely and uniformly hairy
            22. Rachis densely hairy; bark tight, not shaggy . . . .*Carya alba*
            22. Rachis smooth or sparsely hairy; bark shaggy at maturity . . . .*Carya laciniosa*
         21. Leaf undersurface smooth or with tufts of hairs in the vein axils, or sometimes sparsely hairy along the veins
            23. Scales of buds, petiole, and young twigs rusty-hairy or scaly . . . .*Carya texana*

23. Rusty hairs and scales not present
    24. Leaflets mostly 5; bud scales without hairs at the tip; bark tight, not peeling . . .*Carya glabra*
    24. Leaflets mostly 7; bud scales with hairs at the tip; bark sometimes peeling at maturity . . . . . .
    . . . .*Carya ovalis*

1. Leaves opposite
    25. Leaves palmately compound
        26. Leaflets mostly 7; buds very sticky . . . .*Aesculus hippocastanum*
        26. Leaflets mostly 5; buds not sticky
            27. Fruit prickly; flowers yellow . . . . *Aesculus glabra*
            28. Fruit smooth; flowers red . . . . *Aesculus pavia*
            28. Fruit smooth; flowers pale yellow . . . . *Aesculus flava*
    25. Leaves pinnately compound, or sometimes with only 3 leaflets
        29. Leaflets usually 3, or sometimes 5; twigs green or glaucous
        . . . . *Acer negundo*
        29. Leaflets usually 7 or more, sometimes 5; twigs not green
            30. Some or all of the twigs 4-angled . . . .*Fraxinus quadrangulata*
            30. Stems not 4-angled
                31. Leaflets sessile . . . . *Fraxinus nigra*
                31. Leaflets with petiolule
                    32. Leaflet petiolule winged
                        33. Twigs and petioles smooth . . . . *Fraxinus pennsylvanica*
                    32. Leaflets whitened on the lower surface . . . . . *Fraxinus americana*
                    32. Leaflets green or yellow–brown on the lower surface . . . .
        . . . .*Fraxinus profunda*

GROUP C

Leaves broad and flat, never needlelike or scalelike; simple, opposite or whorled

1. Leaves (or some of them) in whorls of 3
  2. Leaves with a bad odor when crushed; flowers with conspicuous purple spots. . . . .*Catalpa bignonioides*
  2. Leaves without a bad odor when crushed; flowers merely lined with purple . . . .*Catalpa speciosa*
1. Leaves opposite
  3. Leaves at least 6 inches long and 6 inches broad, heart-shaped at the base, never palmately lobed . . . .*Paulownia tomentosa*
  3. Leaves usually less than 6 inches long and 6 inches broad, not heart-shaped at the base or if slightly heart-shaped then also palmately lobed
    4. Leaves palmately lobed
      5. Petiole with milky sap when broken . . . .*Acer platanoides*
      5. Petiole without milky sap
        6. Areas between leaf lobes mostly V-shaped; leaves usually silvery or white on the undersurface
          7. Leaves deeply divided, the areas between the lobes extending more than halfway to the midvein . . . .*Acer saccharinum*
          7. Leaves shallowly divided, the areas between the lobes extending less than halfway to the midvein
            8. Leaves completely covered with a white felt on the undersurface . . . .*Acer rubrum* var. *drummondii*
            8. Leaves smooth or sparsely hairy on the undersurface . . . .*Acer rubrum*
        6. Areas between leaf lobes mostly U-shaped; leaves green or paler on the undersurface, not white or silvery
          9. Leaves with the edges drooping
            10. Leaves green on the undersurface; small stipules sometimes present at the base of the petiole . . . . . *Acer nigrum*
            10. Leaves grayish on the undersurface; stipules at the base of the petiole absent . . . . *Acer barbatum*
          9. Leaves flat, the edges not drooping, no stipules . . *Acer saccharum*

4. Leaves not lobed
    11.   Leaves toothed along the edges
        12.   Edges of leaves regularly toothed from tip of leaf to base; leaves usually short-pointed or rounded at the tip
            13.   Buds, petioles, and veins on the undersurface of the leaf covered with rusty hairs . . . .*Viburnum rufidulum*
            13.   Buds, petioles, and veins on the undersurface of the leaf without rusty hairs
                14.   Petioles wavy along the edges . . . .*Viburnum lentago*
                14.   Petioles not wavy along the edges
                    15.   Branches spine-tipped . . . .*Rhamnus cathartica*
                    15.   Branches not spine-tipped . . . .*Viburnum prunifolium*
        12.   Edges of leaves toothed only above the middle of the leaf; leaves tapering to a long point . . . .*Forestiera acuminata*
    11.   Leaves not toothed along the edges
        16.   Upper surface of leaves rough to the touch . . . .*Cornus drummondii*
        16.   Upper surface of leaves smooth
            17.   Leaves with deeply impressed veins on the upper surface; undersurface of leaves gray or whitish
                18.   Leaves often nearly as broad as long; flowers surrounded by 4 large, white bracts; berries red; twigs green to light brown . . . .*Cornus florida*
                18.   Leaves longer than broad; flowers not surrounded by 4 large, white bracts; berries white; twigs gray . . . . . .*Cornus racemosa*
            17.   Leaves without deeply impressed veins; leaves often paler on the undersurface, but not gray or whitish . . . .*Forestiera acuminata*

GROUP D

Leaves broad and flat, never needlelike or scalelike; simple, alternate, neither toothed nor lobed

1. Most or all of the leaves more than 6 inches long
    2. Leaves long-tapering to the base; winter buds elongated, about $1/8$ inch long, covered with reddish brown hairs . . . . *Asimina triloba*
    2. Leaves rounded or only short-tapering to the base; winter buds either $1/2$ inch long and white-hairy or rounded and yellow
        3. Petioles usually more than $1^{1}/2$ inches long, hairy; buds nearly round, yellow . . . . *Nyssa aquatica*
        3. Petioles usually less than $1^{1}/2$ inches long, smooth; buds elongated, white-hairy . . . . *Magnolia acuminata*
1. Most or all of the leaves less than 6 inches long
    4. Petioles with milky sap; twigs usually bearing small spines near the point of leaf attachment . . . . *Maclura pomifera*
    4. Petioles without milky sap; twigs not spiny
        5. Leaves spicy-aromatic when crushed, twigs green . . . . .*Sassafras albidum*
        5. Leaves not spicy-aromatic when crushed; twigs usually not green
            6. Leaves distinctly asymmetrical at base, usually obviously 3-veined from the base
                7. Leaves usually at least twice longer than broad, rounded at the base . . . . *Celtis laevigata*
                7. Leaves usually less than twice longer than broad, more or less heart-shaped at the base . . . . *Celtis tenuifolia*
            6. Leaves symmetrical at the base, with a single main vein
                8. Leaves heart-shaped at the base, about as broad as long . . . . *Cercis canadensis*
                8. Leaves rounded or tapering to the base, longer than broad

9. Many of the leaves clustered near the tips of the twigs
 10. Leaves abruptly short-pointed at the tip. . . . . . .*Nyssa sylvatica*
 10. Leaves tapering to the tip
  11. Veins of leaf deeply impressed, strongly arching toward the tip of the leaf; fruit a drupe . . . .*Cornus alternifolia*
  11. Veins of leaf not deeply impressed nor strongly arching toward the tip of the leaf; fruit an acorn
   12. Undersurface of leaves hairy; petiole usually hairy; leaves usually 1 inch wide or wider. . .*Quercus imbricaria*
   12. Undersurface of leaves smooth except for the veins; petiole usually smooth; leaves usually less than 1 inch wide . . . .*Quercus phellos*
9. Leaves not clustered near the tips of the twigs
 13. Leaves usually with 10 or more pairs of veins; petioles often $1^{1}/2$ inches long or longer . . . .*Nyssa aquatica*
 13. Leaves usually with 6–8 pairs of veins; petioles rarely as long as $1^{1}/2$ inches
  14. Leaves abruptly contracted to a short point at the tip
   15. Leaves usually about twice as long as broad; fruit an orange berry about 1 inch in diameter . . . .*Diospyros virginiana*
   15. Leaves usually less than twice as long as broad; fruit a blue drupe up to $1/2$ inch in diameter . . . . .*Nyssa sylvatica*
  14. Leaves gradually tapering to the tip . . .*Frangula caroliniana*

GROUP E

Leaves broad and flat, never needlelike or scalelike; leaves simple, alternate, toothed but not lobed

1. Leaves asymmetrical at the base
   2. Leaves with 3 main veins arising from the base of the blade
      3. Edge of leaf with low, rounded teeth or merely wavy . . . .*Hamamelis virginiana*
      3. Edge of leaf sharply or finely toothed
         4. Most petioles less than 1 inch long; trunk usually warty
            5. Upper surface of leaf very rough to the touch; leaves thick and leathery
               6. Leaves tapering to a long point at the tip; most or all of the blades 3 inches long or longer . . . .*Celtis occidentalis*
               6. Leaves tapering to a short point at the tip; most or all of the blades less than 3 inches long . . . .*Celtis tenuifolia*
            5. Upper surface of leaf smooth or only slightly rough to the touch; leaves thin and membranaceous
               7. Leaves at least 3 times longer than broad . . . .*Celtis laevigata*
               7. Leaves less than 3 times longer than broad
                  8. Some or all the leaves 3 inches long or longer . . . .*Celtis occidentalis*
                  8. Leaves less than 3 inches long . . . .*Celtis tenuifolia*
         4. Petioles more than 1 inch long
            9. Leaves smooth on the undersurface except for small tufts of hairs where the veins meet . . . .*Tilia americana*
            9. Leaves hairy on the undersurface
               10. Undersurface of leaves white . . . .*Tilia americana* var. *heterophylla*
               10. Undersurface of leaves green. . . . .*Tilia americana*
   2. Leaves with 1 main vein arising from the base of the blade
      11. Some of the twigs with corky wings
         12. Some or all the leaves 4 inches long or longer; petioles more than $1/8$ inch long . . . .*Ulmus thomasii*
         12. None of the leaves 4 inches long; petioles up to $1/8$ inch long . . . .*Ulmus alata*

11. Twigs without corky wings

    13. Leaves very rough to the touch . . . .*Ulmus rubra*

    13. Leaves smooth or soft to the touch

        14. Edge of leaf doubly toothed (each tooth divided into a second small tooth)

            15. Leaves distinctly asymmetrical at the base; petioles often smooth . . . .*Ulmus americana*

            15. Leaves slightly asymmetrical at the base; petioles hairy

                16. Bark of trunk with sinewy ridges; fruit enclosed in flat, 3-lobed bracts; lower lateral veins of leaf unbranched . . . .*Carpinus caroliniana*

                16. Bark of trunk broken into scales; fruit surrounded by inflated, bladdery bracts; lower lateral veins of leaf branched . . . .*Ostrya virginiana*

        14. Edge of leaf singly toothed

            17. Leaves smooth on the undersurface; petioles smooth . . . .*Ulmus pumila*

            17. Leaves hairy on the undersurface, at least where the veins meet; petioles usually hairy . . . .*Planera aquatica*

1. Leaves symmetrical at the base

  18. Leaves with 2–4 irregular teeth along the edges

    19. Leaves usually with 10 or more pairs of veins; petioles often 1½ inches long or longer . . . .*Nyssa aquatica*

    19. Leaves usually with 6–8 pairs of veins; petioles rarely as long as 1½ inches . . . .*Nyssa sylvatica*

  18. Leaves more regularly toothed with more than 4 teeth along the edges

    20. Petioles with milky sap when broken

      21. Petioles and undersurface of leaf with long hairs . . . .*Broussonetia papyrifera*

      21. Petioles and undersurface of leaf smooth or with short hairs

        22. Undersurface of leaf hairy between the veins . . . .*Morus rubra*

        22. Undersurface of leaf smooth or hairy only on the veins. .*Morus alba*

    20. Petioles without milky sap when broken

      23. Leaves at least 4 times as long as broad

        24. Petioles less than ⅛ inch long; leaves irregularly toothed along the edges . . . .*Salix exigua*

        24. Petioles more than ⅛ inch long; leaves regularly toothed along the edges

25. Leaves green on the undersurface . . . .*Salix nigra*
25. Leaves whitish on the undersurface
  26. Each leaf with a pair of leaflike stipules at the base of the
    petiole . . . .*Salix caroliniana*
  26. Each leaf without a pair of leaflike stipules . . . .
    . . . .*Salix amygdaloides*
23. Leaves less than 4 times as long as broad
  27. Leaves as broad as long or broader
    28. Petioles not flattened
      29. Leaves strongly whitened on the undersurface . . .*Populus alba*
      29. Leaves not strongly whitened, pale green on the undersurface .
      . . . .*Populus heterophylla*
      30. Leaf undersurface pale green, often marked with fragrant
      rust-colored blotches . . . .*Populus balsamifera*
    28. Petioles flattened
      30. Leaves basically triangular in shape, coarsely toothed . . . .
      . . . .*Populus deltoides*
      30. Leaves basically ovate or spherical, coarsely or finely toothed
        31. Leaves with 20 or more fine teeth along the edges . . . .
        . . . .*Populus tremuloides*
        31. Leaves with up to 15 coarse teeth along the edges . . . .
        . . . .*Populus grandidentata*
  27. Leaves longer than broad
    32. Twigs usually with sharp spines
      33. Leaves broadest below the middle; fruit a small crabapple
        34. Many of the leaves narrowly oblong to narrowly elliptic . . . .
        . . . .*Malus angustifolia*
        34. Most of the leaves ovate to oval to broadly lance-shaped
          35. Twigs and young leaves densely hairy . . . . .*Malus ioensis*
          35. Twigs and young leaves smooth or nearly so . . . .
          . . . . *Malus coronaria*
      33. Leaves broadest at or above the middle; fruit a hawthorn
        36. Leaves broadest at the middle; petioles 1 inch long
        or longer . . . .*Crataegus viridis*
        36. Leaves broadest above the middle; petioles up to
        3/4 inch long

37. Leaves leathery, smooth on both surfaces ....
...............................*Crataegus crus-galli*

37. Leaves not leathery, usually somewhat hairy on the under
surface ....*Crataegus punctata*

32. Twigs not spiny

38. Some of the twigs with corky wings

39. Some or all the leaves 4 inches long or longer; petioles
more than 1/8 inch long ....*Ulmus thomasii*

39. None of the leaves 4 inches long; petioles up to 1/8 inch
long. ....*Ulmus alata*

38. None of the twigs with corky wings

40. Individual teeth along edge of the leaf at least 1/4 inch long

41. Most of the veins not reaching to the tip of each leaf;
undersurface of leaf usually silvery-white. ....
.... *Quercus bicolor*

41. Most of the veins projecting to the tip of each leaf;
undersurface of leaf green or pale, but usually not
silvery-white

42. Leaves usually with sharp-pointed teeth

43. Fruit an acorn; leaf undersurface usually covered
with very short hairs ....*Quercus muehlenbergii*

43. Fruit enclosed in a prickly bur; leaf undersurface
smooth or nearly so ....*Castanea dentata*

42. Leaves usually with somewhat rounded teeth

44. Cup of acorn at least 1 inch across; trunk whitish to
gray ....*Quercus michauxii*

44. Cup of acorn less than 1 inch across; trunk brown
to black ....*Quercus prinus*

40. Individual teeth along edge of leaf up to 1/8 inch long

45. Some of the leaves produced from short, stubby shoots
along the main twigs ....*Ilex decidua*

45. Twigs without short, stubby side shoots

46. Petioles with 1 or more small glands ("bumps"),
usually near the point of attachment to the blade

47. Each tooth along the edge of the leaf bearing a
    small, reddish brown gland
  48. Some or all leaves 1 inch broad or broader
     49. Leaves flat . . . . *Prunus hortulana*
     49. Leaves more or less folded down the middle . .
       . . . .*Prunus munsoniana*
  48. None of the leaves as wide as 1 inch broad . . . . . .
    . . . .*Prunus angustifolia*
47. Teeth along the edge of the leaf not bearing a gland
  50. Leaves usually with a dull, wrinkled surface; fruit
     a plum . . . .*Prunus americana*
  50. Leaves usually appearing smooth and rather
     shiny; fruit an elongated cluster of small drupes
    51. Teeth along edge of leaf curving inward,
      usually rather blunt . . . . *Prunus serotina*
    51. Teeth along edge of leaf pointing outward,
      usually sharp-pointed. . . . . .*Prunus virginiana*
46. Petioles not bearing glands
  52. Leaves doubly toothed along the edges
    53. Bark peeling off into papery strips or layers;
      leaves usually about 2/3 as broad as long
      or broader
     54. Bark yellowish, silvery gray, or creamy white
      55. Bark yellowish or silvery gray; leaves with
        8 or more pairs of veins . . . .
        . . . .*Betula alleghaniensis*
      55. Bark creamy white; leaves with no more than
        7 pairs of veins . . . .*Betula papyrifera*
     54. Bark reddish brown . . . .*Betula nigra*
    53. Bark broken into small plates, or smooth and
      sinewy, not peeling off into papery strips or layers
     56. Bark of trunk with sinewy ridges; fruit enclosed
      in flat, 3-lobed bracts; lower lateral veins of
      leaf unbranched . . . . *Carpinus caroliniana*
     56. Bark of trunk broken into scales; fruit enclosed
      in inflated, bladdery bracts; lower lateral veins
      of leaf branched . . . .*Ostrya virginiana*

52. Leaves singly toothed along the edges
  57. Leaves heart-shaped at the base
    58. Leaves up to 6 inches long and nearly as broad
      . . . . *Populus heterophylla*
    58. Leaves not more than 4 inches long and about
      $1/2$ as broad
    59. Leaves bronze as they unfold; petiole smooth. . .
      . . . .*Amelanchier laevis*
    59. Leaves densely white-hairy as they unfold;
      petiole somewhat hairy . . . .
      . . . .*Amelanchier arborea*
  57. Leaves rounded or tapering to the base, not heart-
    shaped
    60. Teeth along edge of leaf widely spaced, at least .
      $1/4$ inch apart . . . .*Fagus grandifolia*
    60. Teeth along edge of leaf closely and regularly
      spaced
      61. Petiole hairy; fruit fleshy
        62. Leaves shiny on the upper surface;
          petioles $1/2$ inch long or longer . . . .
          . . . .*Frangula caroliniana*
        62. Leaves dull on the upper surface; petioles
          up to $1/4$ inch long . . . . . .*Planera aquatica*
      61. Petiole smooth at maturity; fruit dry and
        variously winged
      63. Some of the leaves 3 inches long or longer;
        fruit 4-winged or a woody "cone"
        64. Leaves pointed at the tip; fruit 4-winged.
          . . . .*Halesia tetraptera*
        64. Leaves rounded at the tip; fruit a woody
          "cone" . . . .*Alnus glutinosa*
      63. Leaves less than 3 inches long; fruit sur-
        rounded by a flat wing. . . . . .*Ulmus pumila*

GROUP F

Leaves broad and flat, never needlelike or scalelike; leaves simple, alternate, lobed
1. Petioles with milky sap when broken
  2. Petioles and undersurface of leaf with long hairs . . . .
  . . . .*Broussonetia papyrifera*
  2. Petioles and undersurface of leaf smooth or with short hairs
    3. Leaf undersurface hairy between the veins . . . .*Morus rubra*
    3. Leaf undersurface smooth or hairy only on the veins . . . .*Morus alba*
1. Petioles without milky sap when broken
  4. Twigs usually with sharp spines
    5. Leaves broadest at the middle or above the middle
      6. Leaves broadest at the middle; undersurface of leaf smooth except for
      a few tufts of hairs near the veins . . . .*Crataegus viridis*
      6. Leaves broadest above the middle; undersurface of leaf hairy through-
      out . . . .*Crataegus punctata*
    5. Leaves broadest below the middle
      7. Leaves hairy throughout on the undersurface
        8. Leaves mostly tapering to the base; fruit a crabapple (pome) . . . .
        . . . .*Malus ioensis*
        8. Leaves rounded at the base; fruit a hawthorn (pome)
          9. Fruit with pitted seeds; flowers appearing in late May and June . . .
          . . . .*Crataegus calpodendron*
          9. Fruit without pitted seeds; flowers appearing in April or early May
          . . . .*Crataegus mollis*
      7. Leaves smooth on the undersurface or hairy only on the veins
        10. Leaves tapering to the base
          11. Leaves oval to ovate to broadly lance-shaped . . .*Malus coronaria*
          11. Leaves narrowly oblong to narrowly elliptic . .*Malus angustifolia*
        10. Leaves rounded at the base
          12. Leaves blue–green; fruit a hawthorn (pome) . . . .
          . . . .*Crataegus pruinosa*
          12. Leaves green; fruit a crabapple (pome) . . . .
          . . . .*Malus coronaria*

4. Twigs without spines
    13. Leaves star-shaped ....*Liquidambar styraciflua*
    13. Leaves not star-shaped
        14. Leaves 4-lobed, smooth on both surfaces ..... *Liriodendron tulipifera*
        14. Leaves more than 4-lobed, hairy on one or both surfaces
            15. Leaves palmately lobed and veined
                16. Leaves densely coated with white hairs on the undersurface .....
                    ....*Populus alba*
                16. Leaves without a coat of white hairs on the undersurface ....
                    ....*Platanus occidentalis*
            15. Leaves pinnately lobed and veined
                17. Lobes of leaf with bristle-tips
                    18. Leaves broadest above the middle ......*Quercus marilandica*
                    18. Leaves broadest at or below the middle
                        19. Leaves hairy throughout on the undersurface
                            20. Undersurface of leaves with gray hairs; base of leaf
                                blade usually broadly rounded
                                21. Leaves with 5–11 more or less equal lobes, the upper
                                    most lobe not strongly curved ....*Quercus pagoda*
                                21. Leaves with 3–5 more or less unequal lobes, the upper
                                    most lobes often strongly curved .....*Quercus falcata*
                            20. Undersurface of leaves with rusty hairs; base of leaf
                                blade not broadly rounded ....*Quercus velutina*
                        19. Leaves smooth on the undersurface or hairy only next
                            to the veins
                            22. Leaves divided less than halfway to the middle
                                23. Petioles hairy; buds hairy, gray ......*Quercus velutina*
                                23. Petioles smooth; buds smooth, reddish brown ....
                                    ....*Quercus rubra*
                            22. Leaves divided more than halfway to the middle
                                24. Petioles hairy; cup of acorn fringed around the edge ..
                                    ....*Quercus velutina*
                                24. Petioles smooth; cup of acorn not fringed around
                                    the edge
                                    25. Undersurface of leaves with large tufts of hairs in
                                        the vein axils
                                        26. Cup of acorn saucer-shaped

27. Cup of acorn up to $^1/_2$ inch broad . . . .
. . . .*Quercus palustris*

27. Cup of acorn more than $^1/_2$ inch broad . . . .
. . . .*Quercus shumardii*

  26. Cup of acorn top-shaped

    28. Cup of acorn enclosing about $^1/_3$–$^1/_2$ of the
nut; nut often striated . . . .*Quercus texana*

    28. Cup of acorn enclosing $^1/_3$–$^1/_2$ of the
elongated nut . . . .*Quercus ellipsoidalis*

  25. Undersurface of leaves smooth or with small tufts
in hairs in the vein axils . . . .*Quercus coccinea*

17. Lobes of leaf with round tips, not bristle-tipped

  29. Leaves smooth on the undersurface . . . .*Quercus alba*

  29. Leaves hairy on the undersurface

    30. Upper 3 lobes of leaf squarish, forming a cross;
twigs hairy . . . .*Quercus stellata*

    30. Leaves without 3 squarish lobes at the upper end; twigs
smooth or nearly so

      31. Edge of acorn cup with a fringe . . . .*Quercus macrocarpa*

      31. Edge of acorn cup not fringed . . . .*Quercus lyrata*

Key to the Trees of Illinois in Winter

1. Leaves persistent during winter, needlelike or scalelike . . . . .Group A
1. Leaves deciduous . . . . . .Group B

GROUP A

1. Needles in clusters of 2 or more
  2. Needles in clusters of 5 . . . .*Pinus strobus*
  2. Needles in clusters of 2–3
    3. Needles in clusters of 2
      4. Most or all the needles less than 3 inches long, usually twisted
        5. Needles up to $1^{1}/2$ inches long; sheath at base of needles not longer than $1/8$ inch . . . .*Pinus banksiana*
        5. Needles 2–3 inches long; sheath at base of needles at least $1/3$ inch long . . . .*Pinus sylvestris*
      4. Most or all the needles longer than 3 inches, rarely twisted
        6. Needles mostly less than 5 inches long; cone-scale with a small spine

        . . . .*Pinus echinata*
        6. Needles mostly more than 5 inches long; cone-scale without a spine
        . . . .*Pinus resinosa*
    3. Needles in clusters of 3, sometimes 2
      7. Needles flexible, mostly less than 5 inches long; sheath at base of needles about $1/4$ inch long . . . .*Pinus echinata*
      7. Needles stiff, mostly more than 5 inches long; sheath at base of needles about 1 inch long . . . .*Pinus taeda*
1. Leaves solitary
      8. Of 2 types, some scalelike about $1/8$ inch long, some needlelike up . . .
        to $1/3$ inch long . . . .*Juniperus virginiana*
      8. Leaves scalelike, flattened; crushed foliage arromatic.. *Thuja occidentalis*

GROUP B

1. Leaf scars absent (scars which resemble leaf scars present, but lacking bundle scars) . . . .*Taxodium distichum*
1. Leaf scars present
  2. Leaf scars in whorls of 3 . . . .*Catalpa* spp.
  2. Leaf scars opposite or alternate
    3. Leaf scars opposite
      4. Bundle scar 1 . . . .*Forestiera acuminata*
      4. Bundle scars 3 or more
        5. Bundle scars usually 9 or more
          6. Pith hollow or sometimes chambered . . . .*Paulownia tomentosa*
          6. Pith solid, not chambered
            7. Twigs 4-angled, or winged . . . .*Fraxinus quadrangulata*
            7. Twigs circular or oval
              8. First pair of lateral buds inserted some distance below terminal bud . . . .*Fraxinus nigra*
              8. First pair of lateral buds occurring at base of terminal bud
                9. Upper margin of leaf scar straight . . . .*Fraxinus pennsylvanica*
                9. Upper margin of leaf scar usually notched at top or concave
                  10. Twigs with large, conspicuous lenticels; base of tree typically swollen . . . .*Fraxinus profunda*
                  10. Twigs with inconspicuous lenticels; base of tree not typically swollen . . . .*Fraxinus americana*
        5. Bundle scars usually 3–7 (sometimes 9 in *Acer negundo*)
          13. Leaf scars very broad, usually at least $1/3$ inch across
            14. Bark smooth . . . .*Aesculus pavia*
            14. Bark becoming furrowed and scaly
              15. Terminal bud up to $2/3$ inches long, sharp-pointed . . . .*Aesculus glabra*
              15. Terminal bud $3/4$–2 inches long, blunt-pointed . . . .*Aesculus flava*
        13. Leaf scars narrow, less than $1/3$ inch across
          15. Buds with 2 exposed outer scales
            16. Twigs gray or gray–brown

17. Buds long and narrow, at least 5 times longer than broad .
. . . . *Viburnum lentago*
17. Buds shorter, at most 3 times longer than broad
  18. Buds reddish brown
    19. Buds smooth or scurfy . . . . *Viburnum prunifolium*
    19. Buds hairy . . . . *Viburnum rufidulum*
  18. Buds light brown
    20. Buds hairy . . . . *Cornus drummondii*
    20. Buds smooth or nearly so . . . . *Cornus racemosa*
16. Twigs purple or orange–brown
  21. Twigs purplish . . . . *Cornus florida*
  21. Twigs orange–brown, at least usually not purplish . . . .
. . . . *Cornus racemosa*
15. Buds with more than 2 exposed scales
  22. Twigs green or glaucous . . . . *Acer negundo*
  22. Twigs brown, red, or orange
    23. Buds rounded, several in a cluster; twigs red or orange
      24. Twigs hairy . . . . *Acer rubrum* var. *drummondii*
      24. Twigs smooth
        25. Twigs with an unpleasant odor; bark scaly . . . .
. . . . *Acer saccharinum*
        25. Twigs without an unpleasant odor; bark not scaly . . .
. . . . *Acer rubrum*
    23. Buds elongated; twigs brown or gray
      26. Ends of some twigs tapering to a spine . . . .
. . . . *Rhamnus cathartica*
      26. Ends of twigs not spiny
        27. Twigs (at least by the time they are 2 years old)
             pale gray–brown, dull . . . . *Acer nigrum*
        27. Twigs pale reddish brown, shiny
          28. Buds pointed at the tip . . . . *Acer saccharum*
          28. Buds more or less rounded at the tip . . . .
. . . .*Acer barbatum*

3. Leaf scars alternate
   29. Thorns or spines present
      30. Spines in pairs . . . .*Robinia pseudoacacia*
      30. Spines solitary, although sometimes branched
         31. Spines scattered along the twigs and branches . . . .
            . . . .*Aralia spinosa*
         31. Spines not scattered along the twigs and branches
            32. Thorns branched . . . .*Gleditsia* spp.
            32. Thorns unbranched
               33. Buds pointed at the tip
                  34. Twigs usually hairy . . . .*Malus ioensis*
                  34. Twigs usually smooth
                     35. Buds with reddish scales . . . .*Malus coronaria*
                     35. Buds with chestnut brown scales . . .*Malus angustifolia*
               33. Buds more or less rounded at the tip
                  36. Terminal bud absent . . . .*Maclura pomifera*
                  36. Terminal bud present . . . .*Crataegus* spp.

   29. Thorns or spines absent
      37. Pith chambered, at least at the nodes
         38. Leaf scars 3-lobed and usually with 3 groups of bundle scars
            39. Pith pale brown; leaf scars without velvety hairs at the top . . . .
               . . . .*Juglans nigra*
            39. Pith chocolate brown; leaf scars with velvety hairs at the top . .
               . . . .*Juglans cinerea*
         38. Leaf scars half-round, not 3-lobed
            40. Pith chambered only at the nodes; stipular scars present
               41. Buds about 1/4 inch long . . . .*Celtis occidentalis*
               41. Buds about 1/8 inch long
                  42. Twigs usually smooth; tree . . . .*Celtis laevigata*
                  42. Twigs usually hairy; shrub . . . .*Celtis tenuifolia*
            40. Pith chambered between the nodes as well as at most of the
               nodes; stipular scars absent
               43. Exposed bud scales 2 . . . .*Diospyros virginiana*
               43. Exposed bud scales 4 . . . .*Halesia tetraptera*

37. Pith solid, although sometimes with diaphragms
  44. Pith with diaphragms
    45. Buds without bud scales . . . .*Asimina triloba*
    45. Buds with 1 or more scales
      46. Bud scales 1–2; bundle scars 7 or more; stipular scars present
        47. Bud scale 1, hairy . . . .*Magnolia acuminata*
        47. Bud scales 2, smooth . . . .*Liriodendron tulipifera*
      46. Bud scales 3–several; bundle scars 3; stipular scars absent
        48. Buds about 1/4 inch long . . . .*Nyssa sylvatica*
        48. Buds up to 1 inch long . . . .*Nyssa aquatica*
  44. Pith without diaphrams
    49. Bundle scar 1
      50. Twigs yellowish; bark reddish brown . . . .*Larix decidua*
      50. Twigs orange; bark reddish brown . . . .*Larix laricina*
    49. Bundle scars 2 or more
      51. Stipular scars forming a ring around the twig . . . .
        . . . .*Platanus occidentalis*
      51. Stipular scars not forming a ring around the twig, or absent
        52. Twigs aromatic when cut
          53. Twigs green; buds generally smooth . . .*Sassafras albidum*
          53. Twigs orange–brown; buds generally hairy . . . .
            . . . .*Betula alleghaniensis*
        52. Twigs not aromatic when cut
          54. Buds without scales
            55. Terminal buds larger than the rest of the buds
              56. Buds rusty-hairy or gray-woolly
                57. Buds rusty-hairy, 2–3 times longer than broad . . .
                  . . . .*Asimina triloba*
                57. Buds gray-woolly, not much longer than broad . . .
                  . . . .*Malus ioensis*
              56. Buds smooth or, if hairy, not conspicuously
                rusty-hairy or gray-woolly
                58. Leaf scars lobed; twigs without stipular scars
                  59. Buds bright yellow . . . .*Carya cordiformis*
                  59. Buds brown or reddish brown

60. Terminal bud up to $1/2$ inch long; twigs with orange lenticels ....*Carya illinoinensis*

60. Terminal bud up to $1/4$ inch long; twigs with pale lenticels ....*Carya aquatica*

58. Leaf scars unlobed; twigs with stipular scars

61. Buds pale brown; twigs often zigzag ....
.....................*Hamamelis virginiana*

61. Buds light brown; twigs mostly straight ....
.....................*Frangula caroliniana*

55. Terminal buds smaller than other buds or absent

62. Pith reddish brown; leaf scars often $1/2$ inch across
.......................*Gymnocladus dioicus*

62. Pith not reddish brown; leaf scars less than $1/2$ inch across

63. Milky sap present

64. Twigs hairy

65. Twigs velvety; pith yellow. .....*Rhus hirta*

65. Twigs not velvety; pith whitish ....
.......................*Rhus copallina*

64. Twigs smooth ....*Rhus glabra*

63. Milky sap absent

66. Leaf scars completely encircling the bud ....
.....................*Cladrastis kentukea*

66. Leaf scars only partly encircling the bud ....
.......................*Ptelea trifoliata*

54. Buds with 1 or more scales

67. Buds with 1 scale ....*Salix* spp.

67. Buds with 2 or more scales

68. Bundle scar 1

69. Twigs with short spurlike shoots ....
.............................*Ilex decidua*

69. Twigs without short spurlike shoots ....
.....................*Diospyros virginiana*

68. Bundle scars 2 or more

70. Buds at least 4 times longer than broad

71. Stipular scars encircling the twig, or nearly so
.......................*Fagus grandifolia*

71. Stipular scars not encircling the twigs, or absent

72. Undermost bud scale directly above the leaf scar . . . .*Populus deltoides*
72. Undermost bud scale to one side of leaf scar
  73. Twigs reddish brown, with pale lenticels . . . .*Amelanchier arborea*
  73. Twigs gray–brown, with dark lenticels . . . .*Amelanchier laevis*
70. Buds less than 4 times longer than broad (Go to 74)
74. Pith star-shaped, or triangular, or variously lobed in cross section
  75. Undermost bud scale directly above the leaf scar
    76. Twigs densely hairy; bark white . . . .*Populus alba*
    76. Twigs smooth or sparsely hairy
      77. Visible bud scales more than 4
        78. Buds smooth, shiny, brown . . . .*Populus tremuloides*
        78. Buds hairy, dull, gray . . . .*Populus grandidentata*
        78. Visible bud scales 2; terminal bud sticky . . .*Populus balsamifera*
      77. Visible bud scales 3–4
        79. Buds at least 1/2 inch long . . . .*Populus deltoides*
        79. Buds less than 1/2 inch long . . . .*Populus heterophylla*
  75. Undermost bud scale to one side of leaf scar
    80. Buds clustered near the tip of the twig; bud scales in 5 rows
      81. Buds at least 1/4 inch long
        82. Buds angular
          83. Buds smooth . . . .*Quercus shumardii*
          83. Buds hairy, at least at tip
            84. Buds hairy all over
              85. Buds with rusty or brown hairs
                86. Buds with rusty hairs . . . .*Quercus marilandica*
                86. Buds with brown hairs . . . .*Quercus michauxii*
              85. Buds with gray hairs . . . .*Quercus velutina*
             84. Buds hairy only at the tip
              87. Buds light red–brown . . . .*Quercus pagoda*
              87. Buds dark red–brown . . . .*Quercus coccinea*
        82. Buds not angular
          88. Buds and twigs orange–brown . . . .*Quercus prinus*
          88. Buds and twigs red, red–brown, dark brown, or gray–brown
            89. Buds red or red–brown

90. Buds light red to light red–brown . . . .*Quercus rubra*
90. Buds dark red to dark red–brown . . . . .*Quercus falcata*
89. Buds dark brown . . . .*Quercus coccinea*
81. Buds less than 1/4 inch long
91. Buds pointed at the tip
92. Buds and twigs brown to orange–brown . . . .
. . . .*Quercus muehlenbergii*
92. Buds and twigs red to red–brown to gray–brown
93. Scales of buds hairy
94. Twigs dark red–brown to gray; buds reddish brown . . . . . .
. . . .*Quercus falcata*
94. Twigs light or dark brown; buds gray–brown . . . .
. . . .*Quercus imbricaria*
93. Scales of buds smooth or nearly so
95. Buds dark red–brown . . . .*Quercus phellos*
95. Buds light red–brown . . . .*Quercus palustris*
91. Buds more or less rounded
96. Twigs red–brown, shiny; buds not angular . . . . . .*Quercus alba*
97. Buds angular . . . .*Quercus ellipsoidalis*
97. Buds slightly angular; ciliated scales at bud apex . . . .
. . . .*Quercus texana*
96. Twigs gray to yellow–brown to purplish, dull
98. Twigs and buds smooth or nearly so
99. Twigs purplish, with a whitish coating . . . .
. . . .*Quercus bicolor*
99. Twigs gray to yellow–brown . . . .*Quercus lyrata*
98. Twigs and buds hairy
100. Buds red–brown . . . .*Quercus stellata*
100. Buds gray to gray–brown . . . .*Quercus macrocarpa*
80. Buds not clustered near the tip of the twig; bud scale not in 5 rows
101. Bundle scars in more than 3 groups; leaf scars lobed
102. Visible bud scales 2
103. Buds bright yellow . . . .*Carya cordiformis*
103. Bud scales brown or reddish brown
104. Terminal bud up to 1/2 inch long; twigs with orange lenticels
. . . .*Carya illinoinensis*
104. Terminal bud up to 1/4 inch long; twigs with pale lenticels .
. . . .*Carya aquatica*

102. Visible bud scales more than 2
  105. Some or all the terminal buds $1/2$ inch long or longer
    106. Outermost bud scales falling away early, revealing pale
      inner scales; bark not peeling . . . .*Carya alba*
    106. Outermost bud scales persistent; bark peeling
      107. Twigs orange–brown, with orange lenticels . . . .
      . . . .*Carya laciniosa*
      107. Twigs dark brown or red–brown, with pale lenticels . . . .
      . . . .*Carya ovata*
  105. Terminal buds usually less than $1/2$ inch long
    108. Buds rusty-hairy, with silvery or yellow scales . . . .
    . . . .*Carya texana*
    108. Buds smooth or only slightly hairy, without scales
      109. Bark smooth or furrowed, not scaly . . . .*Carya glabra*
      109. Bark becoming scaly . . . .*Carya ovalis*
101. Bundle scars in 3 groups; leaf scars not lobed
  110. Buds up to $1/6$ inch long; twigs bitter to the taste
    111. Pith triangular in cross section . . . .*Alnus glutinosa*
    111. Pith not triangular in cross section
      112. Buds very shiny . . . .*Prunus serotina*
      112. Buds dull . . . .*Prunus virginiana*
  110. Buds longer than $1/6$ inch; twigs not bitter to the taste
    113. Twigs sometimes with corky wings; buds with 4 or more
      exposed scales . . . .*Liquidambar styraciflua*
    113. Twigs without corky wings; buds with 2–3 exposed scales . . .
    . . . .*Castanea dentata*
74. Pith round or nearly so in cross section
  114. Terminal bud present
    115. Buds with 2–3 exposed scales . . . .*Cornus alternifolia*
    115. Buds with 4 or more exposed scales
      116. Bud scales fleshy . . . .*Crataegus* spp.
      116. Bud scales not fleshy . . . .*Prunus* spp.
  114. Terminal bud absent
    117. Leaf scars at least $1/2$ inch across; bundle scars 9 . . . .
    . . . .*Ailanthus altissima*
    117. Leaf scars smaller; bundle scars not 9
      118. Stipular scars absent

119. Leaf scars bordered by hairs . . . .*Cercis canadensis*

119. Leaf scars not hairy . . . .*Gleditsia* spp.

118. Stipular scars present

  120. Exposed bud scales 2

    121. Milky sap present . . . .*Broussonetia papyrifera*

    121. Milky sap absent

      122. Twigs gray or brown . . . .*Tilia americana*

      122. Twigs light red . . . .*Tilia americana* var. *heterophylla*

  120. Exposed bud scales 3 or more

    123. Exposed bud scales 3-4; lenticels horizontal

      124. Twigs with taste of wintergreen . . . .*Betula alleghaniensis*

      124. Twigs without taste of wintergreen

        125. Twigs and buds smooth; bark white . . . .
. . . .*Betula papyrifera*

        125. Twigs and buds somewhat hairy; bark reddish . . . .
. . . .*Betula nigra*

    123. Exposed bud scales more than 4; lenticels more or less circular

      126. Bundle scars not in groups of 3; milky sap present

        127. Buds about 1/4 inch long . . . .*Morus rubra*

        127. Buds about 1/8 inch long . . . .*Morus alba*

      126. Bundle scars in groups of 3; milky sap absent

        128. Exposed bud scales usually about 12 . . . .
. . . .*Carpinus caroliniana*

        128. Exposed bud scales usually about 6

          129. Leaf scars and bundle scars slightly elevated . . . .
. . . .*Ostrya virginiana*

          129. Leaf scars and bundle scars depressed

            130. Buds less than 1/8 inch long . . . .
. . . .*Ulmus pumila*

            130. Buds at least 1/8 inch long

              131. Some of the twigs with corky wings

                132. Buds about 1/4 inch long . . .*Ulmus thomasii*

                132. Buds about 1/8 inch long . . . . . .*Ulmus alata*

              131. None of the twigs with corky wings

                133. Buds rusty-hairy, about 1/4 inch long . . . . . .
. . . .*Ulmus rubra*

                133. Buds light brown, smooth, about inch 1/8 long
. . . .*Ulmus americana*

Key to Illinois Oaks (*Quercus* spp.)[1]

1. White oak family; leaves without bristle tips; bark gray; acorns mature at the end of one season.
   - a. Leaves lobed.
     - i. Acorn cup not enclosing the acorn.
       1. Acorn cup shallow and warty . . . .*Q. alba*
       2. Acorn cup covering ½ of the acorn . . . .*Q. stellata*
     - ii. Acorn cup enclosing more than 2/3 of acorn.
       1. Acorn cup not fringed, cup covering majority of . . . . acorn . . . .*Q. lyrata*
       2. Acorn cup fringed . . . .*Q. macrocarpa*
   - b. Leaves not lobed, coarsely toothed.
     - i. Acorns stalked.
       1. Acorn stalk longer than petiole . . . .*Q. bicolor*
       2. Acorn stalk shorter.
          - a. Acorn cup flat-bottomed; bark similar to that of white oak . . . .*Q. michauxii*
          - b. Acorn cup deep; bark similar to that of northern red oak . . . .*Q. prinus*
     - ii. Acorn, small, sessile, cup deep . . . .*Q. muehlenbergii*

[1]Adapted from Fuller, G.D., and E.E. Nuuttila. 1955. *Forest Trees of Illinois: How to Know Them.* Department of Conservation, Springfield, IL. 71pp.

2. Red oak family; leaves with bristle tips; bark dark; acorns mature at the end of two seasons.
    a. Leaves lobed.
        i. Deeply lobed.
            1. Leaves deep green on both sides.
                a. Acorn cup broad and shallow
                    i. Acorn large . . . . *Q. rubra*
                    ii. Acorn small
                        1. Acorn ovoid . . . .*Q. shumardii*
                        2. Acorn globose . . . .*Q. palustris*
                b. Acorn cup deep
                    i. Cup scales loosely imbricated, winter buds large and hairy . . . . .
                    . . . .*Q. velutina*
                    ii. Cup scales tightly appressed, winter buds smaller and smooth
                        1. Acorn small . . . .*Q. ellipsoidalis*
                        2. Acorn larger
                          a. often with concentric circles near apex . . . .*Q. coccinea*
                          b. often striated . . . .*Q. texana*
            2. Leaves pale green beneath.
                a. Leaves polymorphic, 3–5 lobes . . . .*Q. falcata*
                b. Leaves not polymorphic, 5–11 lobed . . . .*Q. pagoda*
        ii. Shallowly lobed, winter buds rusty hairy . . . .*Q. marilandica*

    b. Leaves entire.
        i. Leaves hairy beneath; acorn sessile . . . .*Q. imbricaria*
        ii. Leaves not hairy; acorn stalked . . . .*Q. phellos*

Key to Illinois Hickories (*Carya* spp.)[1]

1. Bud scales paired, not overlapping; appearing somewhat grooved length-wise; leaflets usually lanceolate, generally curved backwards; nut husks usually winged and thin.

    a. Leaflets 5–9; leaves 6–10 inches long; winter buds yellow; nut smooth, kernel bitter; bark smooth to shallowly fissured . . . .*C. cordiformis*

    b. Leaflets 7–13; leaves 9–13 inches long; winter buds dark brown; nut reddish brown, pear-shaped, kernel bitter; bark shaggy . . . .*C. aquatic*

    c. Leaflets 9–17; leaves 12–20 inches long, winter buds yellow brown, hairy; nut elongated, kernel sweet; bark smooth at first becoming scaly to flaky upon maturity . . . .*C. illinoinensis*

2. Bud scales not paired, overlapping; more than 6; leaflets not re-curved; husks usually not winged; nut thick-shelled.

    a. Buds large; twigs stout; nut usually angled; kernel sweet.

        i. Leaflets 5; leaves 8–14 inches long, tufts of minute hairs in leaflet margins; twigs reddish-brown; bark shaggy . . . .*C. ovata*

        ii. Leaflets 5–9 (usually 7); leaves 15–20 inches long; twigs orange–brown; nut large and reddish brown; bark shaggy . . . .*C. laciniosa*

        iii. Leaflets 7–9; leaves 8–14 inches long and aromatic, rachis hairy; bark interlaced with shallow furrows . . . .*C. alba*

    b. Buds smaller; twigs slender; husk thin, nut rounded or angled.

        i. Leaflets 5–7 (usually 5); leaves 8–12 long; husk pear shaped not splitting to the base, kernel bitter; bark usually smooth . . . .*C. glabra*

        ii. Leaflets 5–7 (usually 7); leaves 8–10 long, rachis reddish color; fruit ovoid, husk winged, splits to base upon maturity, kernel sweet; mature bark deeply furrowed and somewhat shaggy . . . .*C. ovalis*

        iii. Leaflets 5–7 (usually 7); leaves 10–12 inches long; husk thin, conspicuously veined; bark not scaly, but lightly furrowed and ridged . . .*C. texana*

[1]Adapted from Fuller, G.D., and E.E. Nuuttila. 1955. *Forest Trees of Illinois: How to Know Them.* Department of Conservation, Springfield, IL. 71pp.

The Trees of Illinois

Species Descriptions and Illustrations

Illustration by
Clint Patterson

FLORIDA MAPLE
Acer barbatum Michx.

Other names: Southern sugar maple

Growth form: Medium-sized tree, up to 60 feet tall; trunk diameter up to 2 feet; crown rounded

Bark: Smooth and pale brown at first, becoming darker and furrowed when old

Twigs: Slender, brown, smooth or hairy, usually with pale lenticels; leaf scars opposite, U-shaped, with 3 to 7 bundle traces

Buds: Rounded, reddish brown, hairy, up to 1/4 inch long

Leaves: Opposite, simple; blades up to 4 inches long, nearly as broad, palmately 3- to 5-lobed, drooping on the sides, the edges sparsely and coarsely toothed, green and smooth or a little hairy on the upper surface, paler and much hairier on the under-surface; petiole up to 3 inches long, very hairy; autumn colors yellow or orange

Flowers: Polygamo-dioecious; staminate and pistillate borne separately but sometimes on the same tree, in dense clusters, yellowish green, appearing as the leaves unfold

Fruit: Samara; borne in pairs, composed of a wing with a seed at the base, greenish, up to 1 inch long

Wood: Diffuse-porous; heavy, strong, straight-grained, white to light brown

Uses: Limited commercial value in Illinois; high-quality lumber, face veneer, furniture, pulpwood, cabinets, flooring, paneling, interior finishing, railroad crossties, wooden-ware, novelties, butcher's blocks, boxes, crates, handles, sporting and athletic goods, musical instruments, maple syrup and firewood; also planted as an ornamental

Habitat: Moderately well-drained to somewhat poorly drained bottomland forests; often found along river banks, low wet woods and limestone ridges

Range: Native to Illinois; Virginia across southern Illinois to southeastern Oklahoma, south to Texas, east to Florida

Distinguishing features: Florida maple resembles black maple in its drooping leaves but differs by its smaller, thicker leaves and lack of stipules.

Florida Maple

BOXELDER
Acer negundo L.

Other names: Ashleaf maple, Manitoba maple

Growth form: Medium-sized tree, up to 60 feet tall; trunk diameter up to 3 feet; crown wide-spreading

Bark: Light brown, ridged when young, becoming deeply furrowed with age

Twigs: Smooth, green, glaucous, or rarely purplish, shiny, usually with white lenticels; leaf scars opposite, U-shaped, with 5 to 9 bundle traces

Buds: Rounded, white-hairy, up to 1/8 inch long

Leaves: Opposite, pinnately compound, with 3 to 7 leaflets; leaflets elliptic to ovate, up to 4 inches long, about one-half as broad, pointed at the tip, tapering or rounded at the sometimes asymmetrical base, smooth or usually coarsely toothed along the edges or even shallowly lobed, light green and smooth on the upper surface, paler and smooth or hairy on the undersurface

Flowers: Dioecious; staminate and pistillate borne on separate trees, several in a cluster, greenish yellow, appearing as the leaves begin to unfold

Fruit: Samara; borne in pairs, in drooping clusters, composed of a curved wing with a seed at the base, greenish yellow, up to 2 inches long

Wood: Diffuse-porous; moderately heavy, soft, straight-grained, white to light brown

Uses: Limited commercial value; furniture, pulpwood, flooring boxes, crates, woodenware, novelties, maple syrup, firewood, pallets, blocking, and paneling

Habitat: Moderately well-drained to somewhat poorly drained bottomland forests; typically found near streams and other bodies of water

Range: Native to Illinois; Vermont across to Saskatchewan, south to Texas, east to Florida

Distinguishing features: Boxelder most nearly resembles ash spp., but differs by its green, glaucous twigs and its paired fruits.

Boxelder

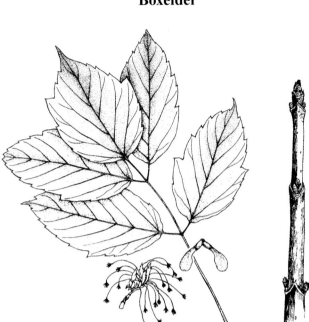

BLACK MAPLE
Acer nigrum Michx. f.

Growth form: Medium-sized to large tree, up to 85 feet tall; trunk diameter up to 2 1/2 feet; crown broad, with several upright branches

Bark: Dark brown to black, smooth when young, soon becoming furrowed and scaly

Twigs: Slender, orange–brown, slightly hairy, often with pale lenticels; leaf scars opposite, U-shaped, with 3 to 7 bundle traces

Buds: Pointed, dark brown, finely hairy, up to 1/4 inch long

Leaves: Opposite, simple; blades up to 6 inches long and nearly as broad, palmately 3- to 5-lobed, drooping on the sides, the edges of the leaves sparsely and coarsely toothed, green and smooth on the upper surface, yellow–green and smooth or hairy on the veins on the undersurface; petiole up to 5 inches long, smooth or hairy, often with stipules at the base; autumn color yellow

Flowers: Polygamous; staminate and pistillate borne separately but sometimes on the same tree, in dense clusters, yellowish, appearing as the leaves unfold

Fruit: Samara; borne in pairs, composed of a wing with a seed at the base, reddish brown to greenish, up to 1 inch long

Wood: Diffuse-porous; heavy, strong, straight-grained, white to light brown

Uses: Valuable timber species; high-quality lumber, face veneer, furniture, baseball bats, cabinets, flooring, paneling, interior finishing, railroad crossties, woodenware, novelties, butcher's blocks, boxes, crates, handles, sporting and athletic goods, musical instruments, maple syrup, pallets, blocking, and firewood; also planted as an ornamental

Habitat: Moderately well-drained to somewhat poorly drained bottomland forests; typically found on rich, moist, well-drained bottomland soils but also thrives on rich upland forest sites. Black maple typically prefers moister sites than sugar maple in Illinois.

Range: Native to Illinois; New Hampshire across to Minnesota and South Dakota, south to Louisiana, east to Georgia

Distinguishing features: Black maple is distinguished from sugar maple by its drooping leaves and stipules at base of the petiole. It differs from Florida maple, which also has drooping leaves, by its larger, thinner leaves.

Black Maple

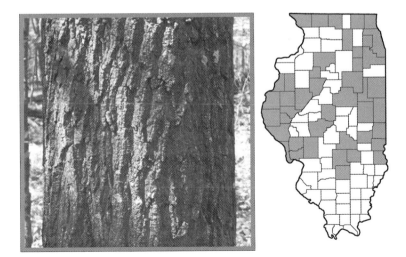

RED MAPLE
Acer rubrum L.

Growth form: Medium-sized tree, up to 80 feet tall; trunk diameter up to 3 feet; crown oval or rounded

Bark: Gray and smooth when young, becoming darker and scaly

Twigs: Slender, mostly smooth, more or less reddish, usually with pale lenticels; leaf scars opposite, U-shaped, with 3 to 7 bundle traces

Buds: Rounded, reddish, usually hairy, up to 1/4 inch long

Leaves: Opposite, simple; blades up to 6 inches long, nearly as broad, palmately 3- to 5-lobed, the edges of the leaves sharply toothed to nearly toothless, pale green and smooth on the upper surface, white or gray and either smooth or hairy on the under-surface; petioles smooth or finely hairy, up to 4 inches long

Flowers: Polygamo-dioecious; staminate and pistillate borne separately but sometimes on the same tree, in dense clusters, bright red or yellow, opening in February and March before the leaves begin to unfold

Fruit: Samara; borne in pairs, composed of an erect wing with a seed at the base, red or yellow, up to 1 inch long

Wood: Diffuse-porous; moderately heavy, straight-grained, light brown to white

Uses: Commercial value; lumber, veneer, furniture, pulpwood, cabinets, railroad crossties, flooring, maple syrup, pallets, blocking, and firewood; extensively planted as an ornamental because of its beautiful autumn foliage

Habitat: A classic generalist; prefers somewhat poorly drained to well-drained bottom-land forests; also thrives in upland forests that range in drainage and fertility

Range: Native to Illinois; Newfoundland across to Ontario, south to eastern Texas, east to Florida

Distinguishing features: Red maple is characterized by its white leaf undersurfaces and its shallowly lobed leaves. The similar silver maple has very deeply lobed leaves.

Red Maple

DRUMMOND MAPLE
Acer rubrum var. *drummondii* (Hook. & Arn. ex Nutt.) Sarg.

Other names: Swamp red maple, Drummond red maple

Growth form: Small tree, up to 40 feet tall; trunk diameter up to 12 inches; crown narrow

Bark: Gray and smooth when young, becoming darker and scaly

Twigs: Slender, white-hairy when young, usually becoming smooth or nearly so, reddish; leaf scars opposite, U-shaped, with 3 to 7 bundle traces

Buds: Rounded, reddish, hairy, up to $1/4$ inch long

Leaves: Opposite, simple; blades up to 6 inches long, nearly as broad, palmately 3- to 5-lobed, the edges of the leaves toothed, green and somewhat hairy on the upper surface, densely white-hairy on the undersurface; petioles stout, densely hairy, up to 4 inches long

Flowers: Polygamo-dioecious; staminate and pistillate borne separately but sometimes on the same tree, in dense red clusters, opening before the leaves begin to unfold

Fruit: Samara; borne in pairs, composed of an erect wing with a seed at the base, bright red, more than 1 inch long

Wood: Diffuse-porous; moderately heavy, straight-grained, white to light brown

Uses: Limited commercial value due to scarcity; lumber, veneer, furniture, pulpwood, cabinets, railroad crossties, flooring, maple syrup, pallets, blocking, and firewood

Habitat: Somewhat poorly drained to poorly drained bottomland forests; often in and around swamps and wetlands

Range: Native to Illinois; New Jersey across to Missouri, south to Texas, east to Florida

Distinguishing features: Drummond maple is distinguished from red maple by the dense coat of white hairs on the undersurface of the leaves and slightly longer samaras.

Drummond Maple

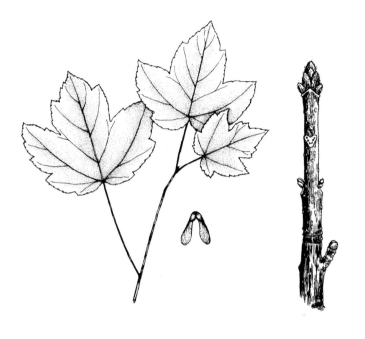

SILVER MAPLE
Acer saccharinum L.

Other names: Soft maple

Growth form: Large tree, up to 100 feet tall; trunk diameter up to 5 feet; crown usually broadly rounded

Bark: Gray or silvery, smooth at first, becoming loose and scaly or even somewhat shaggy when old

Twigs: Slender, reddish brown, smooth, often curving upward; leaf scars opposite, U-shaped, with 3 to 7 bundle traces

Buds: More or less rounded, reddish brown, smooth to finely hairy, up to $1/8$ inch long

Leaves: Opposite, simple; blades up to 8 inches long, nearly as broad, deeply palmately 5-lobed, the edges of the leaves sharply toothed, pale green and smooth on the upper surface, silvery white and usually smooth on the undersurface, except in the leaf axils; petioles smooth, up to 5 inches long, often reddish

Flowers: Polygamous; staminate and pistillate borne separately but sometimes on the same tree, in dense clusters, greenish yellow, opening in February and March before the leaves begin to unfold

Fruit: Samara: borne in pairs, composed of a curved wing with a seed at the base, green or yellow, up to 3 inches long

Wood: Diffuse-porous; moderately heavy, straight-grained, white to pale brown

Uses: Commercial value; lumber, veneer, furniture, pulpwood, cabinets, railroad crossties, flooring, maple syrup, pallets, blocking, and firewood

Habitat: Moderately well-drained to poorly drained bottomland forests; prefers deep, rich alluvial soils

Range: Native to Illinois; New Brunswick across to Minnesota and South Dakota, south to Oklahoma, Texas, east to northern Florida

Distinguishing features: The deeply lobed leaves, which are silvery white on the lower surface, best distinguish this tree.

Silver Maple

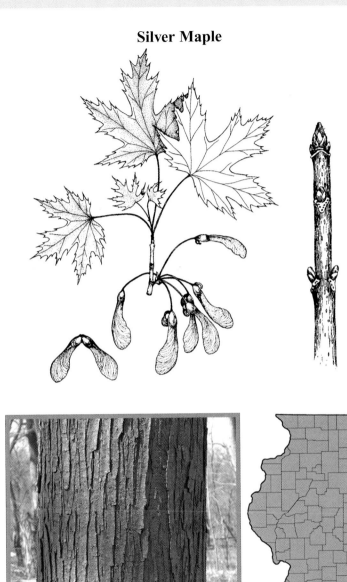

SUGAR MAPLE
Acer saccharum Marsh.

Other names: Hard maple, rock maple

Growth form: Large tree, up to 100 feet tall; trunk diameter up to 3 feet; crown broadly rounded, with many branches

Bark: Gray to dark brown to black, becoming furrowed and scaly

Twigs: Slender, smooth, shiny brown, often with pale lenticels; leaf scars opposite, U-shaped, with 3 to 7 bundle traces

Buds: Pointed, dark brown, smooth, shiny, up to 1/4 inch long

Leaves: Opposite, simple; blades up to 5 inches long, nearly as broad or a little broader, palmately 3- to 5-lobed, the edges of the leaves sparsely and coarsely toothed, dark green and smooth on the upper surface, green or paler on the undersurface and usually smooth, or sometimes hairy on the veins; petioles up to 3 inches long, smooth and sometimes hairy; autumn color yellow and orange

Flowers: Polygamous; staminate and pistillate borne separately but sometimes on the same tree, in dense clusters, greenish yellow, appearing as the leaves begin to unfold

Fruit: Samara; borne in pairs, composed of a wing with a seed at the base, greenish yellow to brownish, up to 1 inch long

Wood: Diffuse-porous; heavy, strong, straight-grained, white to light brown

Uses: A valuable timber species; high-quality lumber, face veneer, furniture, baseball bats, cabinets, flooring, paneling, interior finishing, railroad crossties, woodenware, novelties, butcher's blocks, boxes, crates, handles, sporting and athletic goods, musical instruments, maple syrup, blocking, pallets, and firewood; also planted as an ornamental

Habitat: Well-drained to moderately well-drained upland forests; prefers rich, deep, moist upland sites, including coves, low slopes, and ravines

Range: Native to Illinois; Newfoundland across to Manitoba, south to eastern Texas, east to northern Florida

Distinguishing features: Sugar maple differs from black maple by its leaves and twigs. Sugar maple leaves do not have stipules at the base of its petioles. Sugar maple twigs are usually shinier, with smooth winter buds.

Sugar Maple

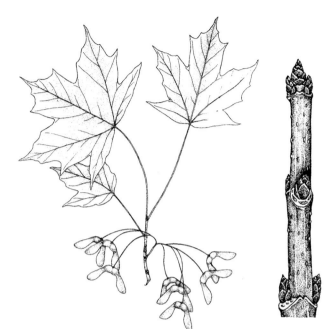

YELLOW BUCKEYE
Aesculus flava Ait.

Growth form: Medium-sized tree, up to 50 feet tall in Illinois; trunk diameter up to 2 feet; crown narrow, pyramidal, with rather small pendulous branches; intermediate growth rate; largest of native buckeyes

Bark: Thin, light brown to grayish brown, scaly, and divided by shallow fissures; breaking up into large, scaly plates

Twigs: Stout, at first hairy, later becoming smooth; leaf scars opposite and large, with several bundle scars arranged in a V-shaped pattern; reddish brown to ashy gray

Buds: Blunt-pointed, 3/4 to 2 inches long, nonresinous; bud scales nearly triangular, outer bud scales reddish brown

Leaves: Opposite, palmately compound, with 5 (sometimes 7) broad-oval, pointed leaflets; leaflets 4 to 8 inches long and 1 1/2 to 3 inches wide, dark green and usually hairless above, yellow–green and often hairy beneath; margins coarsely toothed; petioles slender, 3 1/2 to 7 inches long; autumn color golden yellow

Flowers: Polygamo-monoecious; pale yellow, 1 1/4 inches long, and appear in erect panicles 5 to 6 inches long in spring; petals 4, with the stamens usually shorter than the 2 lateral petals

Fruit: Capsule; smooth-surfaced, leathery, 2 to 3 inches long; more than one-half of the capsules are 1-seeded, although 2-, 3-, and 4-seeded forms are found in decreasing frequencies; ripe seed is dark chocolate to chestnut brown, smooth and shiny, with a large, light-colored hilum

Wood: Diffuse-porous; light, soft and straight-grained, yellowish white

Uses: Limited commercial value in Illinois due to scarcity; lumber, veneer, pulpwood, splints, boxes, crates, caskets, coffins, scientific instruments, novelties, woodenware, and artificial limbs; also planted as an ornamental

Habitat: Well-drained bottomland forests to moderately well-drained upland forests; typically a bottomland species, nevertheless thrives on rich upland forest sites

Range: Native to extreme southeastern Illinois; abundant in Great Smoky Mountains of North Carolina and Tennessee; extends west from the mountains of southwestern Pennsylvania down the Ohio River Valley; south to Kentucky, central Tennessee, and northern Alabama; east to northern Georgia and extreme northwestern South Carolina; and north to western Virginia and West Virginia

Distinguishing features: This tree's leaves are larger than those of Ohio buckeye; twigs and leaves give no off odor when bruised; capsule is smooth, not prickly.

Yellow Buckeye

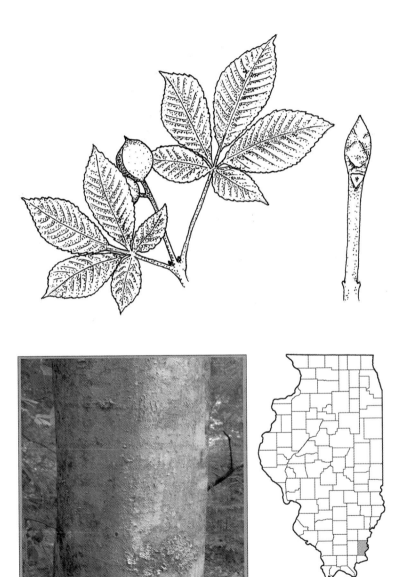

OHIO BUCKEYE
Aesculus glabra Willd.

Growth form: Small to medium-sized tree up to 75 feet tall; trunk diameter up to 2 feet; crown broadly rounded

Bark: Gray to pale gray, smooth and corky ridges on young trees; scaly plates when mature

Twigs: Stout, pale brown, smooth; leaf scars opposite, triangular, with 3 groups of bundle traces

Buds: Ovoid, pointed, reddish brown to yellowish, up to 2/3 inch long, not hairy, not sticky

Leaves: Opposite, palmately compound, with 5 or 7 leaflets; leaflets obovate to oblanceolate, long-pointed at the tip, tapering to the base, up to 6 inches long, less than one-half as wide, toothed along the edges, green and smooth on the upper surface, green or much whitened on the undersurface

Flowers: Polygamo-monoecious, numerous, yellow–green, in large clusters sometimes nearly 1 foot long, appearing in April and May, the petals of each flower of different lengths

Fruit: Capsule; prickly, spherical or nearly so, up to 1 1/2 inch in diameter, pale brown, containing 1 large, smooth and shiny seed

Wood: Diffuse-porous; soft, straight-grained, lightweight, pale brown to nearly white

Uses: Limited commercial timber value; lumber, veneer, and pulpwood

Habitat: Moderately well-drained to somewhat poorly drained bottomland forests; typically a bottomland species, nevertheless thrives on rich upland forest sites

Range: Native to Illinois; Pennsylvania across to Nebraska, south to Oklahoma, east to Alabama

Distinguishing features: Ohio buckeye differs from yellow buckeye by its prickly fruits, and from red buckeye by the greenish yellow flowers and prickly fruits.

Ohio Buckeye

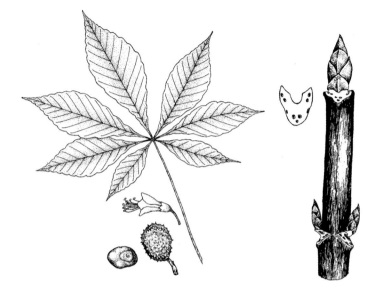

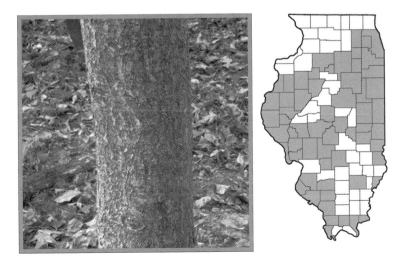

RED BUCKEYE
Aesculus pavia L.

Growth form: Small tree up to 25 feet tall; trunk diameter up to 10 inches; crown rounded and spreading

Bark: Gray to tan, smooth

Twigs: Rather stout, gray to tan, smooth; leaf scars opposite, triangular, with 3 groups of bundle traces

Buds: Ovoid, pointed, reddish brown, up to $1/2$ inch long, not hairy, not sticky

Leaves: Opposite, palmately compound, with 5 leaflets; leaflets elliptic to obovate, pointed at the tip, tapering to the base, up to 6 inches long, less than one-half as wide, toothed along the edges, green and smooth on the upper surface, paler and finely hairy on the undersurface

Flowers: Polygamo-monoecious; numerous, red, in large clusters sometimes nearly 12 inches long, appearing in April

Fruit: Capsule; pear-shaped, leathery, up to 2 inches across, light brown, not prickly, containing 1 or 2 light reddish brown seeds

Wood: Diffuse-porous; soft, straight-grained, lightweight, pale brown to yellowish white

Use: No commercial timber value; planted as an ornamental

Habitat: Prefers rich, well-drained upland and bottomland forests; commonly found along streams, ravines, and wooded bluffs

Range: Native to Illinois; North Carolina across to Missouri, south to Texas, east to Georgia

Distinguishing features: The smooth fruits and the beautiful red flowers distinguish this species from other members of the genus in Illinois.

Red Buckeye

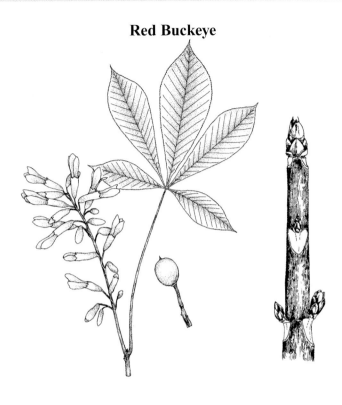

TREE-OF-HEAVEN
Ailanthus altissima (P. Mill.) Swingle

Other names: Ailanthus

Growth form: Medium-sized tree, up to 75 feet tall; trunk diameter up to 2 feet; crown spreading and irregular; readily spreads by underground rootsuckers

Bark: Smooth or slightly roughened, light brown to dark brown

Twigs: Stout, angular, smooth, gray to light brown, with lenticels; leaf scars alternate, large, broadly heart-shaped, slightly elevated, with usually 9 bundle traces

Buds: Rounded, up to $1/8$ inch in diameter, smooth or a little hairy, brown

Leaves: Alternate, pinnately compound, with up to 41 leaflets; leaflets lanceolate, tapering to a long point at the tip, rounded at the base, up to 6 inches long, less than one-half as wide, smooth or somewhat hairy on both surfaces, often with some teeth along the edges; unpleasant odor when crushed

Flowers: Dioecious; in large green or yellow clusters, each flower small, with 5 petals; staminate flowers produce a very unpleasant odor; appear in June and July

Fruit: Samara; large clusters of winged seeds, yellow or orange, each fruit up to 2 inches long with 1 seed about in the middle

Uses: Limited due to this species' invasive nature; not a recommended species to plant

Habitat: Disturbed forests; readily adapts to urban conditions

Range: Introduced (from Asia); exotic and invasive tree found throughout the eastern United States and has become naturalized throughout most of this region

Distinguishing features: The pinnately compound leaves with up to 41 leaflets, unpleasantly scented when crushed, make this a readily recognizable species.

Tree-of-Heaven

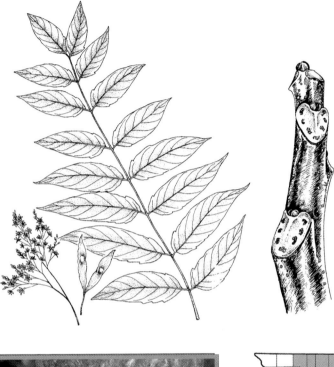

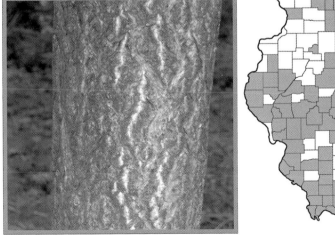

EUROPEAN ALDER
Alnus glutinosa (L.) Gaertn.

Other names: Black alder, European black alder

Growth form: Small to medium-sized tree, up to 45 feet tall; trunk diameter up to 18 inches; crown broadly rounded when mature

Bark: Smooth at first, becoming shallowly fissured with age

Twigs: Slender, gray or gray–brown, smooth; leaf scars alternate, with 3 bundle traces

Leaves: Alternate, simple; blades nearly round or obovate, rounded at the tip, rounded or somewhat tapering to the base, up to 5 inches long, often nearly as broad, irregularly and rather coarsely toothed along the edges, dark green and smooth on the upper surface, green and smooth beneath, or sometimes hairy on the veins; petioles stout, up to 1 inch long, usually smooth

Flowers: Monoecious; staminate and pistillate flowers borne separately but on the same tree, appearing before the leaves unfold; staminate flowers in slender, drooping catkins up to 3 inches long; pistillate flowers in erect, oblong "cones" less than 1 inch long

Fruit: Nutlet; cone-shaped, up to $3/4$ inch long, composed of several nutlike seeds, each subtended by a woody segment of the cone

Wood: Diffuse-porous; soft, straight-grained

Uses: Limited commercial value; wood easily carved and used in the making of small wooden objects; used for charcoal and fuel; bark has reputed medicinal properties; used in mine reclamation because of its nitrogen-fixing properties

Habitat: Typical streamside tree found near lakes, ponds, and ditches in and around municipalities; often found on disturbed sites, especially mine reclamation sites

Range: Introduced (from Europe and Asia); naturalized throughout much of the Midwest, Lake States, and Northeast in the United States

Distinguishing features: The small, woody "cones" and the often orbicular, irregularly toothed leaves are the distinguishing marks of this species.

European Alder

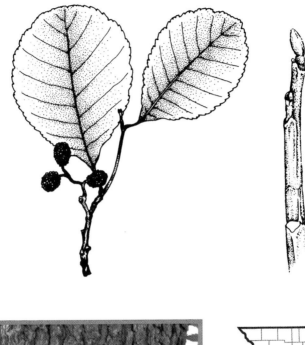

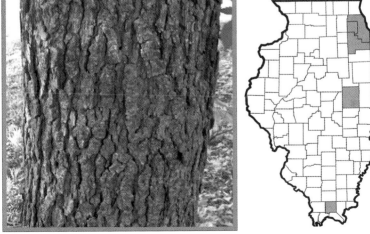

DOWNY SERVICEBERRY
Amelanchier arborea (Michx. f.) Fern.

Other names: Shadbush, shadblow

Growth form: Small tree, up to 20 feet tall; trunk diameter up to 8 inches; crown
rounded and spreading, with many slender branchlets; trunk straight, slender,
often divided into several trunks

Bark: Smooth and silvery at first, later becoming darker and divided into loose scales

Twigs: Slender, brown, with a few hairs when very young; leaf scars alternate,
2-ranked, slightly elevated, narrowly crescent-shaped, with 3 bundle traces

Buds: Pointed, slender, brown, up to $1/2$ inch long

Leaves: Alternate, simple; blades oval to broadly lanceolate, pointed at the tip, rounded
or sometimes a little heart-shaped at the base, finely toothed along the edges, green
and smooth or nearly so on the upper surface, paler and often hairy on the undersurface, up to 4 inches long and about one-half as broad; petioles up to   2 inches
long, smooth or hairy

Flowers: Perfect; several produced in drooping clusters before the leaves appear; each
showy, with 5 white, oblong petals, with much of the flower hairy

Fruit: Pome; mostly spherical, up to $1/4$ inch in diameter, reddish purple, capped by the
persistent calyx, dry, 1- to 2-seeded

Wood: Diffuse to slightly semi-ring-porous; rather heavy, hard, close-grained, reddish
brown

Uses: Fuel, tool handles; fruit edible

Habitat: Wooded slopes; edge of cliffs

Range: Native to Illinois; Quebec across to Minnesota, south to Nebraska, east to
Louisiana and Florida

Distinguishing features: Downy serviceberry is recognized by its alternate, simple
leaves (usually heart-shaped at the base) and distinctive white flowers.

Downy Serviceberry

ALLEGHENY SERVICEBERRY
Amelanchier laevis Wieg.

Other names: Smooth serviceberry, smooth shadbush

Growth form: Small tree, up to 15 feet tall; trunk diameter up to 6 inches; crown narrowly round-topped, with many slender branchlets

Bark: Smooth and gray at first, becoming darker and scaly at maturity

Twigs: Slender, reddish brown or grayish, smooth; leaf scars alternate, slightly elevated, narrowly crescent-shaped, with 3 bundle traces

Buds: Slender, pointed, reddish brown, smooth, up to $3/4$ inch long

Leaves: Alternate, simple; blades elliptic to ovate, pointed at the tip, usually rounded at the base, up to 3 inches long, about one-half as broad, finely toothed along the edges, green and smooth on the upper surface, paler and smooth on the undersurface; petioles slender, up to 1 inch long, smooth

Flowers: Perfect; up to 6 in drooping clusters, appearing after the leaves are one-half grown, each showy with 5 white, narrow petals, with most of the flower smooth

Fruit: Pome; usually spherical, up to $1/4$ inch in diameter, dark purple, sweet, fleshy, 1- to 2-seeded

Wood: Diffuse to slightly semi-ring-porous; hard, heavy, close-grained, dark brown

Uses: Fuel, tool handles; fruit edible

Habitat: Moist forests and slopes

Range: Native to Illinois; Newfoundland across to Ontario, south to Iowa, Illinois, and Georgia

Distinguishing features: Allegheny serviceberry differs from downy serviceberry by its smooth, longer petioles and juicy, edible, dark purple fruits.

Allegheny Serviceberry

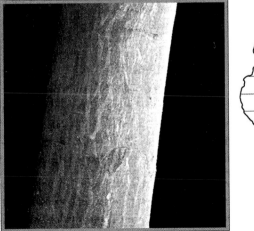

DEVILS-WALKINGSTICK
Aralia spinosa L.

Growth form: Small tree, up to 30 feet tall; trunk diameter up to 6 inches; crown widely spreading

Bark: Dark brown, roughened, shallowly furrowed, with short, hard prickles

Twigs: Stout, pale brown or gray, smooth except for many short, hard prickles; leaf scars alternate, broadly U-shaped, with about 15 bundle traces

Buds: Cone-shaped, brown, smooth, up to 1/2 inch long

Leaves: Alternate, bipinnately compound, with numerous leaflets; leaflets ovate to lance-ovate, pointed at the tip, tapering to rounded at the base, up to 3 inches long, about one-half as wide, coarsely toothed along the edges, green and smooth on the upper surface, paler and smooth on the undersurface, except usually for a few prickles along the veins

Flowers: Perfect; numerous, in many umbrella-shaped clusters, appearing during late June and July, each with 5 small white petals and purple stalks

Fruit: Drupe; black, spherical berries up to 1/8 inch in diameter, containing 2 to 5 seeds

Wood: Lightweight, soft, brittle, close-grained, pale brown and streaked with yellow

Uses: Sometimes grown as an ornamental

Habitat: Rich forests and forest margins

Range: Native to Illinois; New Jersey across to Iowa, south to Texas, east to Florida

Distinguishing features: The clusters of flowers and the leaves each may be as much as 4 feet long. The short, sharp prickles on the twigs are distinctive.

Devils-Walkingstick

PAWPAW
Asimina triloba (L.) Dunal

Growth form: Small tree, rarely up to 40 feet tall; trunk diameter up to 10 inches; crown broad and spreading; trunk straight, slender; thickets develop by means of root suckers

Bark: Dark brown, thin, smooth at first, becoming shallowly fissured with age

Twigs: Slender, smooth, gray; leaf scars alternate, 2-ranked, somewhat horseshoe-shaped, usually with 5 (or less commonly 7) bundle traces

Buds: Very narrow, dark rusty brown, covered with golden hairs, up to $2/3$ inch long, without bud scales

Leaves: Alternate, simple; blades broadly lance-shaped to elliptic, short-pointed at the tip, narrowed to the base, without teeth along the edges, smooth on both surfaces, paler on the undersurface, up to 12 inches long and 6 inches broad; petioles short, slender, smooth

Flowers: Perfect; borne singly when the leaves begin to unfold, up to 2 inches across, green at first, becoming deep maroon; composed of 3 wrinkled, leathery sepals and 6 similar petals. Despite having perfect flowers, pawpaw requires cross-pollination.

Fruit: Berry; oblong, thick, up to 6 inches long (resembles small banana), greenish yellow, with yellow edible flesh and several dark brown seeds, ripening in September; largest native edible fruit in the United States

Wood: Ring-porous with diffuse-porous tendencies; soft, coarse-grained, lightweight, greenish yellow

Uses: Fruit edible; wood has few uses

Habitat: Moderately well-drained to somewhat poorly drained bottomland forests; also thrives on rich, moist upland forest sites

Range: Native to Illinois; New York across to Michigan and Iowa, south to Texas, east to Florida

Distinguishing features: Pawpaw is distinguished by its large, toothless, alternate leaves, slender buds without bud scales, and thick, fleshy, banana-like fruits.

Pawpaw

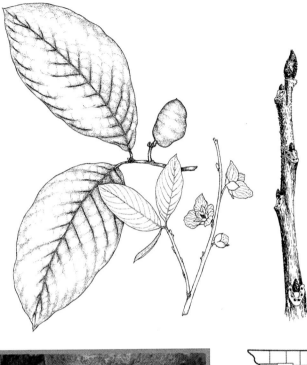

YELLOW BIRCH
Betula alleghaniensis Britt.

Growth form: Small to medium-sized tree, up to 50 feet tall in Illinois; trunk diameter up to 1 1/2 feet; crown broadly rounded, with small branches

Bark: Smooth and silvery or grayish, curling into strips, very rough when old

Twigs: Slender, greenish brown, aromatic, smooth, with numerous lenticels; leaf scars alternate, half-elliptical, with 3 bundle traces

Buds: Pointed, brown, usually somewhat hairy, up to 1/6 inch long

Leaves: Alternate, simple; blades ovate, pointed at the tip, more or less rounded at the somewhat asymmetrical base, up to 5 inches long, and nearly one-half as wide, double-toothed, dark green and nearly smooth on the upper surface, paler and usually somewhat hairy on the undersurface; petioles yellow, hairy, up to 1 inch long; autumn color yellow

Flowers: Monoecious; staminate and pistillate flowers borne separately but on the same tree, appearing after the leaves have begun to unfold; staminate flowers crowded in elongated clusters; pistillate flowers crowded in shorter, thicker clusters

Fruit: Nutlet; several winged nuts, crowded together in erect "cones" up to 1 1/2 inches long

Wood: Diffuse-porous; heavy, hard, strong, light reddish brown

Uses: Limited commercial value in Illinois; high-quality lumber, face veneer, furniture, pulpwood, cabinets, flooring, paneling, interior finishing, railroad crossties, slack cooperage and firewood; one of the principle hardwoods used for distillation of wood alcohol, acetate of lime, charcoal, tar, and oils

Habitat: Well-drained to moderately well-drained upland forests; prefers rich, deep, moist upland sites, including coves, low slopes, and ravines; also found in wetter areas near bodies of water

Range: Native to Illinois; Newfoundland across to Manitoba, south to Iowa, northern Illinois, northern Indiana, Ohio, and Delaware; also in the Appalachian Mountains to Georgia

Distinguishing features: Yellow birch differs from all other birches in Illinois by its silvery or grayish bark and ovate leaves. The bark and fresh twigs have the faint fragrance of wintergreen.

Yellow Birch

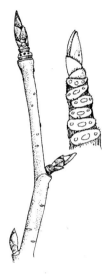

RIVER BIRCH
Betula nigra L.

Other names: Red birch

Growth form: Medium-sized tree, up to 75 feet tall; trunk diameter up to 2 feet; crown irregularly rounded

Bark: Curling, shredding, brownish pink to reddish brown

Twigs: Slender, reddish brown, with several short hairs; leaf scars alternate, half-elliptical, with 3 bundle traces

Buds: Up to $1/4$ inch long, pointed, hairy

Leaves: Alternate, simple; blades rhombic to ovate, coarsely doubly toothed, paler and densely hairy on the undersurface, up to 3 inches long, acute at the tip, truncate or tapering to the base, the petioles woolly

Flowers: Monoecious; staminate and pistillate on same tree, inconspicuous, opening in late April and May; staminate flowers in slender drooping clusters; pistillate flowers in short, conelike, woolly clusters

Fruit: Nutlet; tiny, hairy nuts, each with a 3-lobed wing, crowded together in a cylindrical cone up to $1 1/2$ inches long and $1/2$ inch thick

Wood: Diffuse-porous; strong but lightweight; pale brown

Uses: Commercial value; lumber, veneer, furniture, pulpwood, cabinets, flooring, paneling, interior finishing, railroad crossties, basket hoops, artificial limbs, pallets, blocking, and firewood; successfully planted in surface mine reclamation; planted as an ornamental

Habitat: Moderately well-drained to somewhat poorly drained bottomland forests; commonly found along streams

Range: Native to Illinois; Massachusetts and New Hampshire across to southern Minnesota and eastern Kansas, south to eastern Texas and Florida

Distinguishing features: The shaggy, peeling reddish brown bark readily distinguishes this tree from any other in Illinois, as does its rhombic, doubly toothed leaves.

River Birch

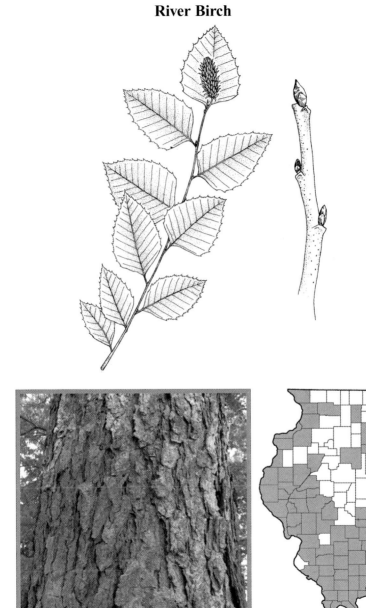

PAPER BIRCH
Betula papyrifera Marsh.

Other names: White birch

Growth form: Medium-sized tree, up to 70 feet tall; trunk diameter up to 2 feet; crown broadly rounded, irregular, with many slender branches

Bark: Thin and white or creamy, splitting at maturity into papery layers, becoming very dark and furrowed near the base of the trunk at maturity

Twigs: Slender, zigzag, reddish brown to blackish, somewhat hairy; leaf scars alternate, half-elliptical, with 3 bundle traces

Buds: Slender, pointed, dark brown, smooth or nearly so, up to $1/4$ inch long

Leaves: Alternate, simple; blades ovate, pointed at the tip, somewhat at the base, up to 3 inches long, more than one-half as wide, coarsely toothed, dark green and smooth on the upper surface, yellow–green and smooth or somewhat hairy on the undersurface and with black dots on the undersurface; petioles yellow, smooth or finely hairy, up to 1 inch long; autumn color yellow

Flowers: Monoecious; staminate and pistillate borne separately on the same tree, developing in the autumn and present on the tree during the winter; staminate flowers crowded into slender spikes up to 4 inches long; pistillate flowers minute, without petals, crowded into thicker spikes up to $1^1/4$ inches long

Fruit: Nutlet; conelike, cylindrical, drooping, composed of many minute seeds attached to 3-lobed wings

Wood: Diffuse-porous; lightweight, strong, durable, straight-grained, light reddish brown

Uses: Bark used to cover canoes; wood used for lumber, pulp, fuel, toothpicks, and spools; sometimes grown as an ornamental

Habitat: Rich, wooded slopes and stream banks

Range: Native to Illinois; Labrador across to Alaska, south to Montana, Colorado, northern Illinois, and West Virginia

Distinguishing features: Paper birch is readily distinguished by its white bark, which peels off into thin, papery layers.

Paper Birch

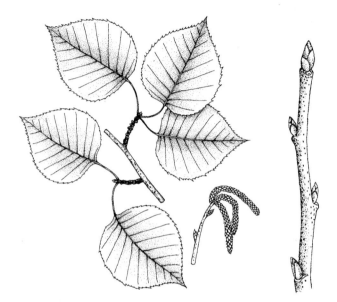

PAPER MULBERRY
Broussonetia papyrifera (L.) L'Hér. ex Vent.

Growth form: Small tree, up to 20 feet tall; trunk diameter up to 8 inches; crown rounded

Bark: Gray or light brown, smooth

Twigs: Moderately stout, greenish gray, smooth or finely hairy, zigzag; leaf scars alternate, nearly spherical, elevated, with 5 bundle traces

Buds: Cone-shaped, somewhat smooth, up to $1/8$ inch long

Leaves: Alternate, simple; blades ovate, tapering to a point at the tip, more or less heart-shaped at the base, up to 8 inches long, sometimes nearly as broad, toothed, sometimes 2- or 3-lobed, usually rough-hairy on both surfaces; petioles up to 2 inches long, smooth or finely hairy

Flowers: Monoecious or dioecious; staminate and pistillate flowers borne separately, on separate trees, appearing as the leaves unfold; staminate flowers in pendulous catkins; pistillate flowers in dense, hairy, spherical heads

Fruit: Spherical, semi-fleshy, orange, up to 1 inch in diameter, with red fruits projecting

Wood: Soft, brittle

Use: Often planted as an ornamental

Habitat: Alongside roads, around old homesites

Range: Introduced (from Asia); occasionally found alongside roads and within fencerows in the eastern United States

Distinguishing features: The fruit of paper mulberry is quite different than that of white and red mulberry. The leaves of paper mulberry are rougher and hairier than those of red mulberry.

Paper Mulberry

AMERICAN HORNBEAM
Carpinus caroliniana Walt.

Other names: Musclewood, blue-beech

Growth form: Small tree, up to 30 feet tall; trunk diameter up to 1 1/2 feet;
crown rounded

Bark: Smooth, blue–gray, ridged, appearing "muscular"

Twigs: Slender, difficult to break, reddish brown, smooth or finely hairy;
leaf scars alternate, crescent-shaped, elevated, with 3 bundle traces

Buds: Small, angular, tapering to a short point

Leaves: Alternate, simple; blades thin, pointed at the tip, usually rounded at the base,
2 to 4 inches long and about one-half as wide, finely doubly toothed, the upper surface smooth, the undersurface either smooth or hairy; petioles up to 1/2 inch long,
hairy

Flowers: Monoecious; staminate and pistillate on same tree but in different catkins,
opening during May

Fruit: Nutlets; borne at the base of a 3-lobed green "leaf," crowded together into a
fruiting cluster

Wood: Diffuse-porous; strong, hard, heavy, pale yellow to tan

Uses: Limited commercial value; tool handles, mallets, levers, wedges, and firewood

Habitat: Well-drained bottomland forests to moderately well-drained upland forests;
prefers rich, deep, moist sites, including coves, low slopes, and ravines

Range: Native to Illinois; Nova Scotia across to central Minnesota, south to eastern
Oklahoma and eastern Texas, east to central Florida

Distinguishing features: Several other trees may be confused with the American hornbeam: American beech, which has smooth gray bark, leaves with fewer teeth, and
twigs with pointed buds; eastern hophornbeam, which has similar leaves but flaky
bark; and elm, which also has somewhat similar leaves but an asymmetrical base.

American Hornbeam

MOCKERNUT HICKORY
Carya alba (L.) Nutt. ex Ell.

Other names: White hickory

Growth form: Large tree, up to 90 feet tall; trunk diameter up to 3 feet; crown rounded, the branchlets either erect or hanging

Bark: Dark gray, shallowly furrowed, not scaly, often with a diamond-shaped pattern

Twigs: Slender or relatively stout, usually hairy, gray; leaf scars alternate, 3-lobed, not elevated, with several bundle traces

Buds: Ovoid, rounded or pointed at the tip, up to ¾ to 1 inch long, reddish brown, hairy

Leaves: Alternate, pinnately compound, with 5 to 9 leaflets; leaflets broadly lanceolate to oblanceolate, pointed at the tip, rounded or tapering to the base, up to 8 inches long, about one-half as wide, finely toothed along the edge, yellow–green and hairy on the upper surface, paler and hairy on the undersurface

Flowers: Monoecious; staminate and pistillate borne separately but on the same tree, appearing after the leaves have begun to unfold; minute, without petals; staminate flowers crowded in slender, drooping catkins; pistillate flowers in groups of 2 to 5

Fruit: Nut; ellipsoid or obovoid or spherical, up to 2 inches across, the husk reddish brown, up to $1/4$ inch thick, smooth or slightly hairy, the nut sometimes 4-angled, reddish brown, the seed sweet but small

Wood: Ring-porous; heavy, hard, strong, coarse-grained, pale brown to reddish brown

Uses: A valuable timber species; tool handles, lumber, veneer, furniture, pulpwood, cabinets, flooring, interior finishing, agricultural implements, baseball bats, gymnasium apparatus, pallets, blocking, smoking meats, and firewood

Habitat: A classic generalist; thrives in rich, well-drained upland and bottomland forests; more commonly found growing on somewhat excessively drained ridges and uplands

Range: Native to Illinois; Massachusetts across to southern Ontario, south to eastern Texas, east to Florida

Distinguishing features: Mockernut hickory is distinguished from all other Illinois hickories by its usual 7 to 9 hairy leaflets with hairy rachis and hairy twigs. The large fruits with the small seeds within, which may account for the common name, also are distinctive.

Mockernut Hickory

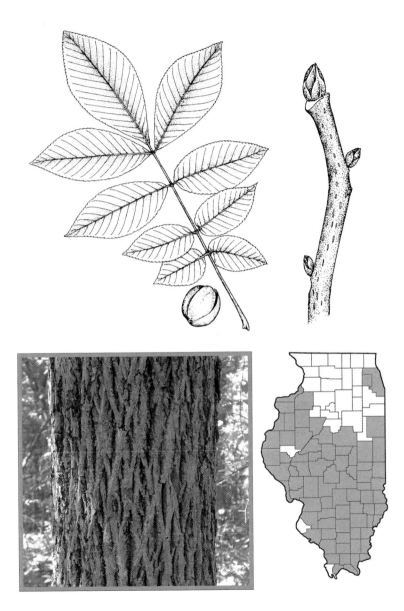

WATER HICKORY
Carya aquatica (Michx. f.) Nutt.

Growth form: Medium-sized tree up to 75 feet tall; trunk diameter up to 2 feet; crown narrow

Bark: Reddish brown, becoming somewhat scaly at maturity

Twigs: Slender, reddish brown or gray, smooth or occasionally slightly hairy; leaf scars alternate, 3-lobed, scarcely elevated, with several bundle traces

Buds: Pointed, reddish brown with yellow scales, usually hairy, up to 1/4 inch long

Leaves: Alternate, pinnately compound, with 7 to 17 leaflets; leaflets lance-shaped, curved, pointed at the tip, tapering to the asymmetrical base, up to 5 inches long, up to 2 inches wide, finely toothed along the edges, dark green and smooth or nearly so on the upper surface, brownish and smooth or somewhat hairy on the undersurface

Flowers: Monoecious; staminate and pistillate borne separately but on the same tree, appearing when the leaves are partly grown; staminate flowers several, in slender, drooping catkins up to 3 inches long; pistillate flowers fewer, in shorter spikes; neither type with petals

Fruit: Nut; short-ellipsoid, usually tapering to either end, flattened, up to 1 1/2 inches long and two-thirds as broad; husk 4-winged, dark brown but with yellow scales, thin, splitting only about halfway to the base; nut flattened, 4-angled, reddish brown, husk thin, seed bitter

Wood: Ring-porous; heavy, hard, strong, close-grained, to reddish brown

Uses: Limited commercial value in Illinois; tool handles, furniture, pulpwood, pallets, blocking, smoking meats, and firewood

Habitat: Somewhat poorly drained to poorly drained bottomland forests; common to swamps, poorly drained flats, and sloughs in backwater basins

Range: Native to Illinois; Virginia across to southeastern Missouri, south to Texas, east to Florida

Distinguishing features: Water hickory is similar to pecan and bitternut hickory in having seven or more leaflets per leaf. However, it lacks the yellow buds of the bitternut hickory and the slender, edible nut of the pecan. The leaves are generally hairier than those of the pecan.

Water Hickory

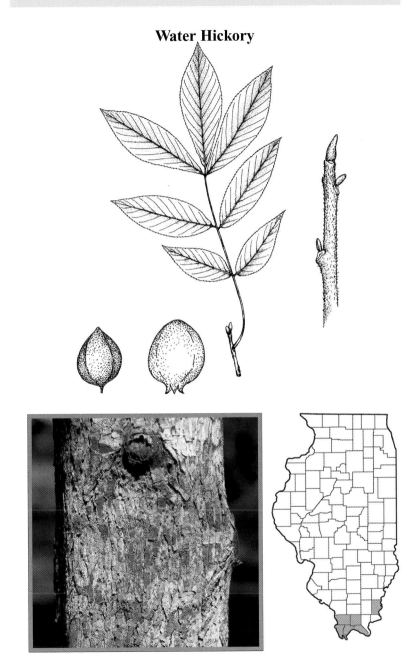

BITTERNUT HICKORY
Carya cordiformis (Wangenh.) K. Koch

Other names: Yellow-bud hickory

Growth form: Large tree, up to 100 feet tall; trunk diameter up to $2^1/_2$ feet; crown broadly rounded and often irregular; trunk straight, columnar

Bark: Gray, thin, separating into shallow ridges and fissures

Twigs: Slender, grayish or orange–brown, smooth, usually with lenticels; leaf scars alternate, shield-shaped, scarcely elevated, with usually several bundle traces

Buds: Narrow, slender, pointed, covered by a dense, bright yellow coat of glandular dots and small hairs, up to $^3/_4$ inch long

Leaves: Alternate, pinnately compound, with usually 7 to 9 leaflets; leaflets lance-shaped, usually curved, long-pointed at the tip, tapering or rounded at the base, toothed along the edges, yellow–green and smooth on the upper surface, somewhat lighter and usually hairy on the undersurface, up to 6 inches long and usually less than one-half as wide

Flowers: Monoecious; staminate and pistillate borne separately but on the same tree, appearing after the leaves have begun to unfold; minute, without petals; staminate flowers in slender, drooping catkins; pistillate flowers single or in pairs

Fruit: Nut; more or less spherical, up to $1^1/_4$ inches in diameter; husk thin, yellowish, with 4 distinct ridges extending about halfway down; nut somewhat flattened, smooth; seed very bitter

Wood: Ring-porous; heavy, hard, strong, white to red–brown

Uses: A valuable timber species; tool handles, lumber, veneer, furniture, pulpwood, cabinets, flooring, interior finishing, pallets, blocking, smoking meats, and firewood

Habitat: A classic generalist; thrives in rich, well-drained to somewhat excessively drained upland forests and rich, well-drained to somewhat poorly drained bottom-land forests; arguably the most widely and uniformly distributed hickory in the United States

Range: Native to Illinois; southern Ontario across to central Minnesota, south to eastern Texas, east to north-central Florida

Distinguishing features: Bitternut hickory is easily recognized by its slender, mustard yellow buds. It differs further from the water hickory by its rounded fruits.

Bitternut Hickory

PIGNUT HICKORY
Carya glabra (P. Mill.) Sweet

Growth form: Large tree, up to 100 feet tall; trunk diameter up to 3 feet; crown oblong or obovoid, with many small, spreading branchlets; trunk straight, columnar, sometimes branching fairly low to the ground

Bark: Light gray to dark brown, sometimes scaly or peeling off into shreds, at maturity furrowed and ridged

Twigs: Slender, brown or gray, shiny, smooth, tough, usually with lenticels; leaf scars alternate, shield-shaped or 3-lobed, scarcely elevated, usually with several bundle traces

Buds: More or less rounded but coming to a short point at the tip, tan or grayish, the outermost scales tipped with a few small hairs, never with small yellow dots; the inner scales hairy all along the edges, up to $1/2$ inch long

Leaves: Alternate, pinnately compound, with usually 5 (sometimes 7) leaflets; rachis green; leaflets lance-shaped, pointed at the tip, tapering at the bottom, toothed along the edges, green and smooth on the upper surface, glabrous below, up to 5 inches long and up to 2 inches broad, the upper 3 leaflets larger than the lower 2

Flowers: Monoecious; staminate and pistillate borne separately but on the same tree, appearing after the leaves have begun to expand; minute, without petals; staminate flowers in slender, drooping catkins; pistillate flowers in groups of 1 to 3

Fruit: Nut; spherical to pear-shaped, up to 1 inch long, not quite as broad; husk thin, greenish, usually not splitting all the way to the base; nut somewhat compressed and with a very hard shell; seed bitter; occasionally trees have fruits up to 2 inches long

Wood: Ring-porous; heavy, strong, hard, white to reddish brown

Uses: A valuable timber species; tool handles, lumber, veneer, furniture, pulpwood, cabinets, flooring, interior finishing, agricultural implements, baseball bats, gymnasium apparatus, pallets, blocking, smoking meats, and firewood

Habitat: Somewhat excessively drained to moderately well-drained upland forests; characteristically an upland species

Range: Native to Illinois; Vermont across to southern Michigan and northern Illinois, south across Missouri to eastern Texas, east to central Florida

Distinguishing features: Pignut hickory is best differentiated from red hickory by its rather small leaflets (usually five in number), characteristic pear-shaped fruits, and green rachis.

Pignut Hickory

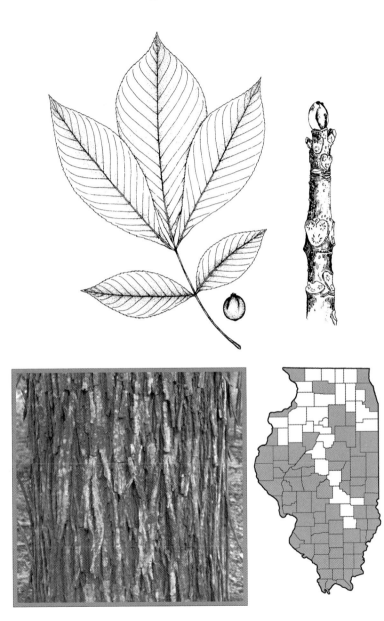

PECAN
Carya illinoinensis (Wangenh.) K. Koch

Growth form: Large tree up to 120 feet tall; trunk diameter up to 3 feet; crown widely spreading and rounded; trunk rather short, stout, straight

Bark: Reddish brown to gray–brown, becoming roughened into platy scales

Twigs: Rather stout, brown, hairy when young but becoming smooth; leaf scars alternate, 3-lobed, scarcely elevated, with 3 to 18 bundle traces

Buds: Long-pointed, covered with yellow glandular dots and fine hairs, up to $1/2$ inch long

Leaves: Alternate, pinnately compound, with 9 to 19 leaflets; leaflets lance-shaped, curved, long-pointed at the tip, rounded or tapering to the asymmetrical base, finely doubly toothed, yellow–green and usually smooth on the upper surface, paler and either smooth or hairy on the undersurface, up to 8 inches long and 3 inches broad

Flowers: Monoecious; staminate and pistillate borne separately but on the same tree, appearing when the leaves are partly grown; staminate flowers many, in slender, drooping, yellow–green catkins; pistillate flowers fewer, in shorter spikes; neither type with petals

Fruit: Nut; ellipsoid, pointed at the tip, up to 2 inches long and 1 inch broad; husk narrowly 4-winged, dark brown but with yellow scales, thin, usually splitting nearly to the base; nut pointed at the tip, reddish brown with black markings; shell thin; seed sweet

Wood: Ring-porous; hard, heavy, coarse-grained, white to red–brown

Uses: A valuable timber species; tool handles, lumber, veneer, furniture, pulpwood, cabinets, flooring, interior finishing, pallets, blocking, smoking meats, and firewood; highly prized for its edible nuts

Habitat: Moderately well-drained to somewhat poorly drained bottomland forests; attains its best development on deep, fertile, well-drained alluvial soils

Range: Native to Illinois; Indiana to Iowa, south through southeastern Kansas to eastern Texas, east to Alabama; Mexico

Distinguishing features: Pecan differs from all other hickories by its greater number of leaflets. Black walnut and butternut, which may have as many leaflets, have a partitioned pith. In every case, the fruit of the pecan is distinctive.

Pecan

SHELLBARK HICKORY
Carya laciniosa (Michx. f.) G. Don

Other names: Kingnut hickory

Growth form: Large tree, up to 100 feet tall; trunk diameter up to 3 feet; crown oblong to ovoid, with drooping lower branches; trunk straight, columnar, stout

Bark: Light gray, soon separating into long, thick, vertical plates that curve away from the trunk

Twigs: Stout, gray or brown, conspicuously dotted with orange lenticels; leaf scars alternate, shield-shaped or 3-lobed, not elevated, usually with several bundle traces

Buds: Elongated, dark brown, hairy, up to $1^1/4$ inches long; the outer scales with a long, stiff point

Leaves: Alternate, pinnately compound, with 5 to 9 leaflets (usually 7); leaflets lance-shaped to ovate, pointed at the tip, tapering or rounded at the base, finely toothed along the edges, dark green and mostly smooth on the upper surface, paler and softly hairy on the undersurface, up to 10 inches long and up to one-half as wide

Flowers: Monoecious; staminate and pistillate borne separately but on the same tree, appearing after the leaves have begun to unfold; minute, without petals; staminate flowers in slender, drooping catkins; pistillate flowers in clusters of 2 to 5

Fruit: Nut; spherical, often depressed at the top, up to $2^1/4$ inches across; husk divided all the way to the base into 4 sections; minutely orange-speckled and sometimes hairy; nut with conspicuous ridges; seed very sweet

Wood: Ring-porous; heavy, hard, close-grained, white to red–brown

Uses: A valuable timber species; tool handles, lumber, veneer, furniture, pulpwood, cabinets, flooring, interior finishing, agricultural implements, baseball bats, gymnasium apparatus, pallets, blocking, smoking meats, and firewood

Habitat: Moderately well-drained to somewhat poorly drained bottomland forests; attains its best development on deep, fertile, well-drained alluvial soils; also found on rich upland sites

Range: Native to Illinois; southwestern Pennsylvania and southern Michigan across to central Illinois and southern Iowa, south to northeastern Oklahoma, Arkansas, and eastern Tennessee; also in scattered areas of New York, Virginia, North Carolina, Georgia, Alabama, and Mississippi

Distinguishing features: The shaggy bark and large leaflets resemble those of shagbark hickory, but the shellbark hickory has orange-dotted twigs, usually seven leaflets, which lack minute tufts of hairs in leaf margins, and much larger fruit.

Shellbark Hickory

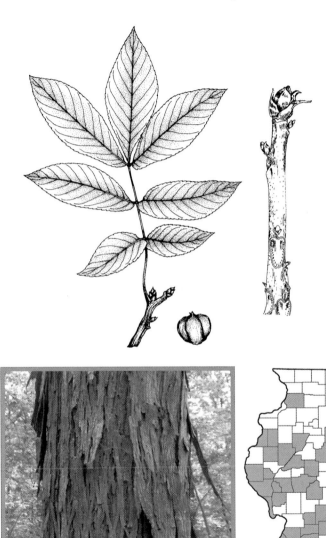

RED HICKORY

Carya ovalis (Wangenh.) Sarg.

Other names: Sweet pignut hickory

Growth form: Medium-sized to large tree, up to 100 feet tall; trunk up to 3 feet in diameter; crown oblong or broadly rounded; with upright, spreading upper branches and drooping lower branches; trunk straight, columnar

Bark: Gray to reddish gray, tight and rather smooth when young, sometimes peeling off into narrow plates at maturity; bark on mature trees displays ridged or furrowed bark instead of peeling bark

Twigs: Slender, brown or gray, tough, smooth, usually with lenticels; leaf scars alternate, 3-lobed, not elevated, usually with several bundle traces

Buds: More or less rounded but coming to a short point at the tip, tan or grayish, usually minutely yellow-dotted, the scales hairy all along the edges, up to $2/3$ inch long

Leaves: Alternate, pinnately compound, with usually 7 (sometimes 5) leaflets; red rachis; leaflets lance-shaped, sometimes curved, pointed at the tip, tapering or somewhat rounded at the base, finely toothed along the edges, green and smooth on the upper surface, pubescent below, up to 6 inches long, up to 2 inches broad

Flowers: Monoecious; staminate and pistillate borne separately but on the same tree, after the leaves have begun to unfold; minute, without petals; staminate flowers crowded in slender, drooping catkins; pistillate flowers borne singly or in pairs

Fruit: Nut; ellipsoid, rarely spherical, up to $1^{1}/4$ inch long; husk green, usually winged and minutely warty, thin, splitting all the way to the base; seed sweet

Wood: Ring-porous; heavy, hard, white to red–brown

Uses: A valuable timber species; tool handles, lumber, veneer, furniture, pulpwood, cabinets, flooring, interior finishing, agricultural implements, baseball bats, gymnasium apparatus, pallets, blocking, smoking meats, and firewood

Habitat: Somewhat excessively drained to moderately well-drained upland forests; characteristically an upland species

Range: Native to Illinois; New Hampshire across to Wisconsin, south to Arkansas, east to Georgia

Distinguishing features: Although it cannot always be reliably distinguished from pignut hickory, red hickory usually has ridged to tightly furrowed bark, seven leaflets, minutely yellow-dotted buds, red rachis, and a winged husk that splits to the base.

Red Hickory

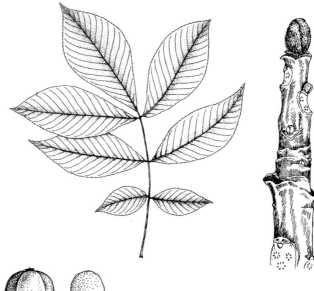

SHAGBARK HICKORY
Carya ovata (Mill.) K. Koch

Growth form: Large tree, up to 100 feet tall; trunk diameter up to $3^1/2$ feet; crown rounded, with some of the branches often hanging

Bark: Gray, separating into long, shreddy plates, giving the trunk a shaggy appearance

Twigs: Stout, reddish brown to gray, smooth or somewhat hairy; leaf scars alternate, 3-lobed, not elevated, with several bundle traces

Buds: Ovoid, rounded or short-pointed at the tip, up to 1 inch long, hairy, the scales conspicuously yellow–green or reddish as they unfold in the spring

Leaves: Alternate, pinnately compound, with 5 (sometimes 7) leaflets; leaflets ovate, obovate, or less commonly lance-shaped; usually short-pointed at the tip, tapering to the base, up to 10 inches long, up to 5 inches wide, finely toothed along the edges, with the tip of each tooth with a minute tuft of hairs, green or yellow–green, smooth on the upper surface; paler and smooth or somewhat hairy on the undersurface

Flowers: Monoecious; staminate and pistillate borne separately but on the same tree, appearing after the leaves have begun to unfold; minute, without petals; staminate flowers crowded in slender, drooping catkins; pistillate flowers in groups of 2 to 5

Fruit: Nut; spherical, up to 2 inches across; husk yellow–green to reddish brown, up to $1/2$ inch thick, splitting all the way to the base; nut 4-angled, nearly white; seed sweet

Wood: Ring-porous; heavy, hard, close-grained, white to red–brown

Uses: A valuable timber species; tool handles, lumber, veneer, furniture, pulpwood, cabinets, flooring, interior finishing, agricultural implements, baseball bats, gymnasium apparatus, pallets, blocking, smoking meats, and firewood

Habitat: Well-drained to moderately well-drained upland forests; occasionally found on terraced bottomland forests with excellent drainage

Range: Native to Illinois; Maine across to Minnesota, south to eastern Texas, east to Florida

Distinguishing features: Shagbark hickory is distinguished by its shaggy bark, its usually five large leaflets, and its large winter buds.

Shagbark Hickory

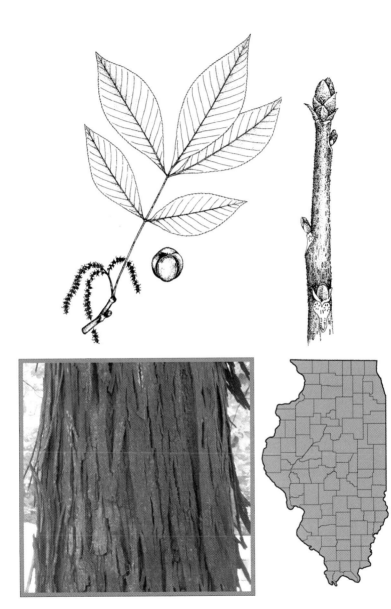

BLACK HICKORY
Carya texana Buckl.

Other names: Texas Hickory

Growth form: Small to medium-sized tree, up to 60 feet tall; trunk diameter up to 2 feet; crown oblong to rounded, with numerous small branchlets

Bark: Brown to black, not scaly or peeling off into shreds, becoming somewhat furrowed and ridged at maturity

Twigs: Slender, gray, tough, almost always smooth; leaf scars alternate, 3-lobed, not elevated, usually with several bundle traces

Buds: Ovoid, short-pointed, up to $1/2$ inch long, covered by shiny silvery golden scales and tipped with a small tuft of hairs

Leaves: Alternate, pinnately compound, with 5 to 9 leaflets; leaflets lance-shaped, pointed at the tip, tapering to the base, finely toothed along the edges, dark green and smooth or sometimes hairy on the upper surface, paler and smooth or hairy on the lower surface, up to 6 inches long, less than one-half as wide, the petioles covered with reddish and yellowish scales and hairs

Flowers: Monoecious; staminate and pistillate borne separately on the same tree, appearing after leaves have begun to unfold; minute, without petals; staminate flowers crowded in slender, drooping catkins; pistillate flowers borne singly or in pairs

Fruit: Nut; spherical to ellipsoid, up to $1 1/2$ inches across; husk yellow–green, thin, minutely hairy or scaly, splitting nearly to the base; nut 4-angled; seed sweet

Wood: Ring-porous; heavy, hard, white to red–brown

Uses: Limited commercial value in Illinois; tool handles, furniture, pulpwood, pallets, blocking, smoking meats, and firewood

Habitat: Excessively drained to well-drained upland forests; characteristic of dry, gravelly, sandy soils with low fertility

Range: Native to Illinois; southern Indiana across to Kansas, south to Texas and Louisiana

Distinguishing features: Black hickory differs from the somewhat similar red and pignut hickories by the yellow scales along the petioles.

Black Hickory

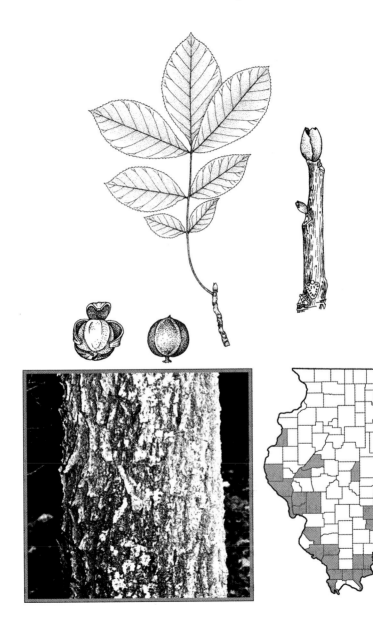

AMERICAN CHESTNUT
Castanea dentata (Marsh.) Borkh.

Growth form: Formerly a large tree, attaining heights in excess of 100 feet; trunk diameter up to 3 feet; crown broadly rounded; now typically reduced to stump sprouts

Bark: Dark brown, shallowly furrowed

Twigs: Slender, reddish brown, angular, glabrous or nearly so; leaf scars alternate, half-round, elevated, with several bundle traces

Buds: Ovoid, pointed, up to $1/3$ inch long, dark brown, smooth

Leaves: Alternate, simple; blades lanceolate to oblong-lanceolate, pointed at the tip, tapering to the base, up to 8 inches long and less than one-half as broad, coarsely toothed along the edges, yellow–green and smooth on the upper surface, paler and smooth on the lower surface; petioles up to $1/2$ inch long, usually finely hairy

Flowers: Monoecious; staminate and pistillate borne separately but on the same tree, appearing in June after the leaves are fully grown, without petals, greenish or yellowish; staminate flowers many and in elongated catkins up to 8 inches long; pistillate flowers, 1 to 3 together

Fruit: Nut; spiny bur up to 2 inches in diameter, brown, splitting open to reveal 3 flattened nuts

Wood: Ring-porous; soft, lightweight, grayish brown to dark brown

Uses: Timbers and lumber often reclaimed from historical structures; furniture, flooring, interior finishing; nuts are edible delicacies

Habitat: A classic generalist; occurs on a wide variety of sites and soils

Range: Native to Illinois; Maine to southern Ontario and southern Minnesota, south to Delaware, Kentucky, and southern Illinois, and in the mountains to central Alabama

Distinguishing features: In addition to its large, spiny fruits, American chestnut can be distinguished by its sharply toothed leaves.

American Chestnut

SOUTHERN CATALPA
Catalpa bignonioides Walt.

Other names: Cigar tree, Indian bean, catawba tree

Growth form: Medium-sized tree, up to 60 feet tall; trunk diameter up to 2 feet; crown broadly rounded

Bark: Light brown, with thin, platy scales

Twigs: Stout, smooth or slightly hairy, orange–brown to grayish, with conspicuous lenticels; leaf scars in whorls of 3, round-elliptic, elevated, with 12 or more bundle traces

Buds: Round, reddish brown, slightly hairy, very small

Leaves: Whorled, simple; blades ovate, short-pointed at the tip, heart-shaped at the base, up to 8 inches long and about as broad, smooth along the edges, yellow–green and smooth on the upper surface, paler and finely hairy on the undersurface; petioles stout, smooth, up to 6 inches long; strong odor when bruised

Flowers: Perfect; large, showy, several in a large cluster, appearing in May and June, the clusters usually more than 6 inches long, each flower up to 2 inches long, petals white and spotted with purple

Fruit: Capsule; beanlike, elongated capsules up to 6 to 15 inches long and $1/2$ inch thick, brown, splitting into 2 parts to reveal several winged, hairy seeds about 1 inch long

Wood: Usually ring-porous; lightweight, soft, straight-grained, pale brown

Uses: Fence posts, railroad ties; ornamental plantings

Habitat: Along railroads, streams, in fields; planted elsewhere

Range: Introduced (from the southern United States); native from Texas to Georgia and Florida; widely planted as an ornamental

Distinguishing features: See northern catalpa.

Southern Catalpa

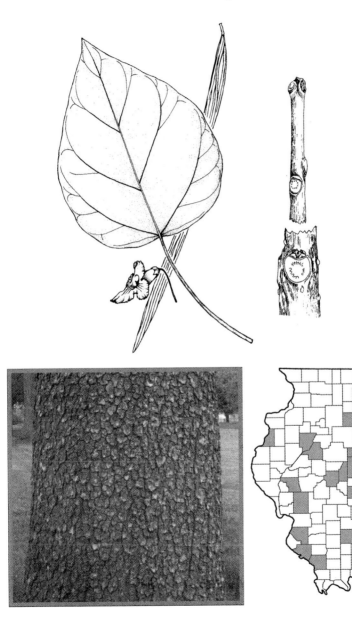

NORTHERN CATALPA
Catalpa speciosa (Warder) Warder ex Engelm.

Other names: Western catalpa, cigar tree, Indian bean, catawba tree

Growth form: Medium-sized tree, up to 80 feet tall; trunk diameter up to 3 feet; crown broad, widely spreading

Bark: Light brown, dark brown, or black; usually with rather deep furrows, sometimes with flat scaly ridges

Twigs: Stout, smooth, brown, with conspicuous lenticels; leaf scars in whorls of 3, with 1 of the 3 scars smaller than the other 2, round-elliptic, elevated, with 12 or more bundle traces

Buds: True terminal bud lacking; round, brown to black, smooth, very small

Leaves: Whorled, simple; blades ovate, long-pointed at the tip, heart-shaped at the base, up to 1 foot long and about two-thirds as broad, smooth along the edges, dark green and smooth or sparsely hairy on the upper surface, soft-hairy on the undersurface; petioles stout, up to 6 inches long; no strong odor when bruised.

Flowers: Perfect; large, showy, several in an elongated cluster, appearing in May and June, the clusters up to 6 inches long; each flower up to $2^{1}/_2$ inches long, petals white and lined with purple

Fruit: Capsule; beanlike, elongated, up to 18 inches long and $3/4$ inch thick, brown, splitting into 2 parts to reveal several winged, hairy seeds about 1 inch long

Wood: Usually ring-porous; lightweight, soft, straight-grained, pale brown

Uses: Fence posts, interior finishing, railroad ties; ornamental plantings

Habitat: Bottomland forests; often planted in a variety of habitats

Range: Native to Illinois; southern Indiana, southern Illinois, and southern Missouri; south to Texas, Arkansas, and Tennessee; commonly planted elsewhere

Distinguishing features: The two catalpas in Illinois are difficult to tell apart. This species usually has deeply furrowed bark, shorter clusters of flowers, petals merely lined with purple rather than spotted.

Northern Catalpa

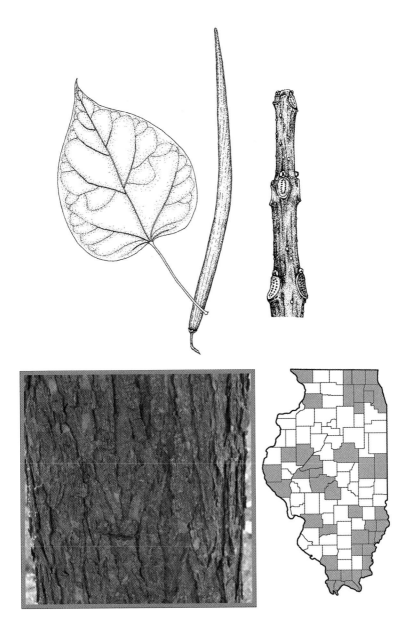

SUGARBERRY
Celtis laevigata Willd.

Other names: Southern hackberry, sugar hackberry

Growth form: Medium-sized to large tree, up to 80 feet tall; trunk diameter up to $2^1/2$ feet; crown open and broad, with drooping branches

Bark: Gray, with many conspicuous wartlike growths

Twigs: Slender, gray or reddish brown, smooth, sometimes zigzag; leaf scars alternate, usually crescent-shaped, slightly elevated, with 3 bundle traces

Buds: Slender, pointed, smooth, brown or gray, up to $1/8$ inch long

Leaves: Alternate, simple; blades usually lance-shaped, long-pointed at the tip, tapering or rounded at the asymmetrical base, up to 6 inches long, less than one-half as broad, with few or no teeth along margin, usually smooth or barely roughened on 1 or both surfaces; petioles up to $1/2$ inch long, smooth or hairy

Flowers: Polygamo-monoecious; 1 to several in drooping clusters, appearing after the leaves are partly grown, greenish yellow, without petals

Fruit: Drupe; fleshy, ellipsoid to nearly round, reddish orange to yellowish, about $1/4$ inch in diameter, with 1 seed, ripening in September or October, borne on slender, drooping stalks

Wood: Ring-porous; heavy, moderately hard, straight-grained, pale yellow to light brown, sometimes whitish

Uses: Commercial value; lumber, veneer, furniture, pulpwood, slack cooperage, millwork, athletic equipment, crates, boxes, pallets, blocking, and firewood

Habitat: Thrives in rich, well-drained to somewhat poorly drained bottomland forests and in rich, well-drained upland forests

Range: Native to Illinois; Virginia across to southern Missouri, south to Texas, east to Florida

Distinguishing features: Sugarberry differs generally from other hackberries by its narrower, mostly toothless leaves.

Sugarberry

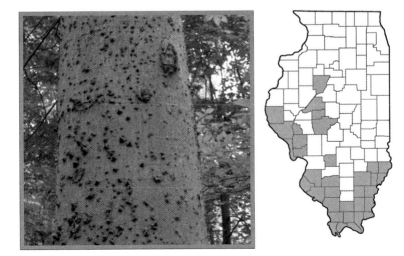

HACKBERRY
Celtis occidentalis L.

Growth form: Large tree, up to 100 feet tall; trunk diameter up to 5 feet; crown usually oblong, with many small branchlets

Bark: Gray, smooth on young trees and soon bearing "warts," becoming rough and scaly on old trees

Twigs: Slender, gray to reddish brown, smooth, sometimes zigzag; leaf scars alternate, usually crescent-shaped, with 3 bundle traces

Buds: Slender, oval, pointed, brown or gray, finely hairy, about 1/4 inch long

Leaves: Alternate, simple; blades ovate or broadly lance-shaped, long-pointed at the tip, rounded or tapering at the asymmetrical base, up to 6 inches long and up to one-half as broad, usually coarsely toothed along the edges except sometimes near the base, smooth or more often rough-hairy on 1 or both surfaces; petioles up to 1 inch long, smooth or hairy

Flowers: Polygamo-monoecious; arranged in drooping clusters, or sometimes solitary, appearing after the leaves are partly grown, greenish yellow, without petals

Fruit: Drupe; fleshy, nearly round, dark purple, about 1/3 inch in diameter, with 1 seed, ripening in September and October, borne on slender, drooping stalks

Wood: Ring-porous; heavy, moderately hard, straight-grained, pale yellow to light brown, sometimes whitish

Uses: Commercial value; lumber, veneer, furniture, pulpwood, slack cooperage, mill-work, athletic equipment, crates, boxes, pallets, blocking, and firewood

Habitat: Moderately well-drained to somewhat poorly drained bottomland forests; typically a bottomland species, nevertheless thrives on rich to somewhat dry upland forest sites

Range: Native to Illinois; Massachusetts across to Manitoba and South Dakota, southern Oklahoma, Alabama and Virginia

Distinguishing features: Hackberry leaves resemble those of some elms but have three main veins arising from the base of the blade. This species differs from other hackberries in Illinois by its larger, usually coarsely toothed leaves and larger, dark purple fruits.

Hackberry

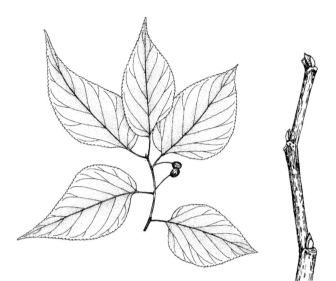

GEORGIA HACKBERRY
Celtis tenuifolia Nutt.

Other names: Dwarf hackberry

Growth form: Small tree, to 25 feet tall; trunk diameter up to 10 inches; crown irregular, with numerous slender branchlets

Bark: Gray, smooth on young trees and soon bearing "warts," becoming rough and scaly on old trees

Twigs: Slender, green to reddish brown, smooth at maturity; leaf scars alternate, crescent-shaped, with 3 bundle traces

Buds: Slender, oval, pointed, grayish brown, finely hairy, up to $1/8$ inch long

Leaves: Alternate, simple; blades ovate, pointed at the tip, rounded or somewhat heart-shaped at the base, up to 3 inches long, often at least one-half as broad, with a few coarse teeth along margins, or sometimes lacking teeth; often leathery, smooth or hairy on 1 or both surfaces; petioles up to $1/2$ inch long, smooth or hairy

Flowers: Polygamo-monoecious; 1 or a few in drooping clusters, appearing after the leaves are partly grown, finely hairy, greenish yellow, without petals

Fruit: Drupe; fleshy, spherical, reddish purple, up to $1/2$ inch in diameter, 1-seeded, ripening September and October

Wood: Ring-porous; moderately heavy, straight-grained, yellowish

Uses: Fence posts, fuelwood; ornamental plantings

Habitat: Understory of hardwood forests

Range: Native to Illinois; New Jersey across to Illinois and Kansas, south to Oklahoma, Louisiana, and northern Florida

Distinguishing features: This small tree is extremely variable in that its leaves may or may not have toothed margins, they may or may not be hairy, and they may or may not be leathery. It differs from the sugarberry primarily by its broader leaves and from hackberry by its smaller fruits and usually less-toothed leaves.

Georgia Hackberry

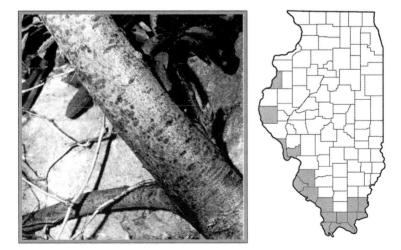

EASTERN REDBUD
Cercis canadensis L.

Other names: Redbud, judas tree

Growth form: Small tree, up to 35 feet tall; trunk diameter up to 1 foot; crown usually broad and flattened

Bark: Reddish brown, separating into long plates and thin scales

Twigs: Slender, zigzag, smooth, angular, brown; leaf scars alternate, somewhat elevated, triangular, hairy across the top, with 3 bundle traces

Buds: Small, rounded, chestnut brown, smooth or nearly so

Leaves: Alternate, simple; blades heart-shaped, contracted to a short point at the tip, up to 6 inches long and nearly as broad, smooth on the upper surface, smooth or with some hairs on the undersurface, without teeth along the edges; petioles slender, up to 5 inches long, usually smooth

Flowers: Perfect; in small clusters on last year's branches or on the trunks, rose–purple, each pea-shaped, about $1/2$ inch long, appearing when the leaves are first beginning to unfold

Fruit: Legume; up to 4 inches long and $1/2$ inch broad, flat, smooth, brown at maturity, with several seeds

Wood: Ring-porous; hard, heavy, close-grained, dark reddish brown

Uses: No commercial value; firewood, wood turning; highly prized as an ornamental

Habitat: Well-drained to moderately well-drained upland forests; also found on slopes extending into bottomland forests; typically a forest understory or edge tree

Range: Native to Illinois; Connecticut across to southern Wisconsin, south to Texas, east to northern Florida; also Mexico

Distinguishing features: The heart-shaped, toothless leaves easily identify this tree.

Eastern Redbud

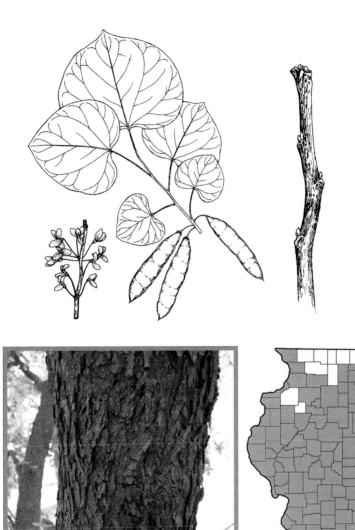

YELLOWWOOD
Cladrastis kentukea (Dum.-Cours.) Rudd

Growth form: Small to medium-sized tree, up to 65 feet tall; trunk diameter up to 14 inches; crown widely spreading

Bark: Gray, smooth (similar to American beech)

Twigs: Slender, reddish brown, with some lenticels, somewhat zigzag; leaf scars alternate, narrow, and completely encircling the bud, with 3 to 7 bundle traces

Buds: 3 to 4 crowded together, resembling at first a single bud, hairy, without scales, covered at first by the hollow base of the petiole

Leaves: Alternate, pinnately compound, with 7 to 11 leaflets; leaflets oval, pointed at the tip, tapering to the base, up to 4 inches long and up to one-half as wide, smooth on both surfaces, toothless along the edges; autumn color yellow

Flowers: Perfect; long, drooping clusters up to 1 foot, white, slightly fragrant, appearing during June

Fruit: Legume; up to 4 inches long and about $1/2$ inch wide, flat, smooth, pale brown, with 4 to 6 seeds

Wood: Semi-ring-porous; hard, heavy, strong, close-grained, yellow to light brown

Uses: Limited commercial value; veneer, lumber, gunstocks, and firewood; historically, as a yellow dye

Habitat: Well-drained to moderately well-drained upland forests; also found on slopes extending into bottomland forests

Range: Native to Illinois; North Carolina across to southern Missouri and Arkansas, south to northern Alabama and northern Georgia

Distinguishing features: The large, pinnately compound leaflets and the smooth, gray trunk distinguish this tree.

Yellowwood

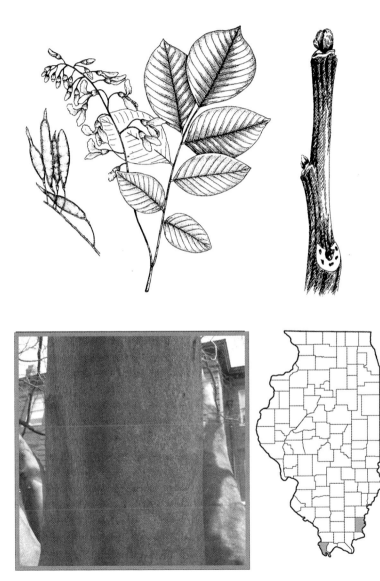

ALTERNATE-LEAF DOGWOOD
Cornus alternifolia L. f.

Growth form: Small tree, up to 20 feet tall; trunk diameter up to 3 inches; crown flattened

Bark: Brown, slightly roughened, with shallow furrows

Twigs: Slender, reddish brown or greenish, smooth; leaf scars alternate, crescent-shaped, somewhat elevated, with 3 bundle traces

Buds: Narrowly ovoid, pointed, smooth, up to $1/4$ inch long

Leaves: Alternate, although often clustered toward the tip of the twig, simple; blades oval to ovate, pointed at the tip, tapering or rounded at the base, up to 5 inches long, about one-half as broad, the edges smooth or finely round-toothed; green and mostly smooth on the upper surface, paler and frequently hairy on the undersurface; petioles up to 2 inches long, usually finely hairy

Flowers: Perfect; several in crowded round-topped clusters, appearing in May and June; each flower white, with 4 narrow petals

Fruit: Drupe; blue, spherical berries up to $1/3$ inch in diameter, borne on a red stalk

Wood: Diffuse-porous; heavy, hard, interlocked-grain, brown to reddish brown

Uses: Tool handles, novelty items, firewood; ornamental plantings

Habitat: Rich forests

Range: Native to Illinois; Newfoundland across to southern Ontario and Minnesota; south to Missouri, Alabama, and Georgia

Distinguishing features: This is the only American dogwood with leaves arranged in an alternate manner, hence its common name.

Alternate-leaf Dogwood

ROUGHLEAF DOGWOOD
Cornus drummondii C.A. Mey.

Growth form: Small tree, up to 30 feet tall; trunk diameter up to 6 inches; crown open and irregular

Bark: Reddish brown, scaly, shallowly furrowed

Twigs: Slender, pale brown, purplish, or gray; smooth or slightly hairy; leaf scars opposite, crescent-shaped, slightly elevated, with 3 bundle traces

Buds: Slender, flattened, pointed, finely hairy, up to $1/8$ inch long

Leaves: Opposite, simple; blades elliptic to narrowly ovate, pointed at the tip, tapering to rounded at the base, up to 4 inches long, up to one-half as wide, smooth along the edges, green and with short hairs on the upper surface, paler and hairy on undersurface; petioles up to $1/2$ inch long, hairy

Flowers: Perfect; several in round-topped clusters, appearing in May and June, each flower white, with 4 narrow petals

Fruit: Drupe; white, spherical berries up to $1/4$ inch in diameter, borne on red stalks

Wood: Diffuse-porous; hard, heavy, interlocked-grain, brown to reddish brown

Uses: Tool handles, firewood; ornamental plantings

Habitat: Forests; edges of prairies

Range: Native to Illinois; New York across to Minnesota, south to Nebraska and Texas, east to Florida

Distinguishing features: This is the only dogwood in Illinois that is rough-hairy on the upper surface of the leaves.

Roughleaf Dogwood

FLOWERING DOGWOOD
Cornus florida L.

Growth form: Small to medium tree, up to 40 feet tall; trunk diameter rarely more than 2 feet; crown rounded

Bark: Brown, divided into small, squarish plates

Twigs: Slender, greenish to light brown, smooth, often curving upward at the tip; leaf scars opposite, crescent-shaped, elevated, with 3 bundle traces

Buds: Of 2 kinds; leaf buds slender, pointed; flower buds flat and biscuit-shaped

Leaves: Opposite, simple; blades elliptic to ovate, pointed at the tip, tapering or rounded at the base, up to 6 inches long, less than one-half as broad, veins deeply impressed, edges without teeth, green and smooth or sparsely hairy on the upper surface, pale and finely hairy or sometimes smooth on the undersurface; petioles up to $3/4$ inch long, smooth or finely hairy

Flowers: Perfect; several crowded together in a yellow–green cluster, each cluster subtended by 4 large white petal-like bracts, appearing in mid April and May

Fruit: Drupe; red, ovoid berries up to $1/2$ inch long, shiny, with mealy flesh and 1 to 2 seeds

Wood: Diffuse-porous; hard, strong, heavy, interlocked-grain, brown to reddish brown

Uses: Tool handles, shuttles and bobbins, firewood; highly valued ornamental

Habitat: Rich forests

Range: Native to Illinois; Maine across to Kansas, south to Texas, east to Florida; also in Mexico

Distinguishing features: The opposite, toothless leaves with deeply impressed veins distinguish this species.

Flowering Dogwood

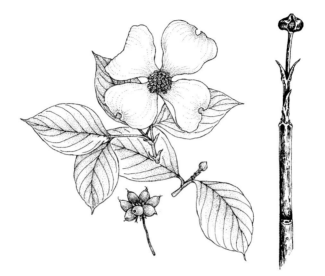

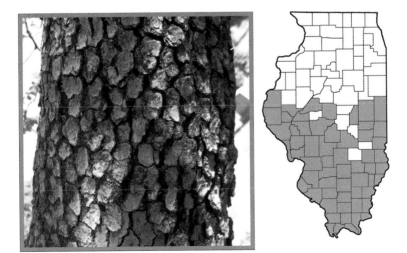

OTHER DOGWOODS

Several other dogwoods, most of them rarely if ever attaining the stature of small trees, occur in Illinois.

Gray Dogwood (*Cornus racemosa* Lam.). This plant rarely exceeds a height of 10 feet. It is distinguished by its slender gray twigs, small white flowers borne in clusters about as broad as high, and white berries about 1/4 inch in diameter. This dogwood occurs in a variety of habitats, including prairies and forests.

Stiff Dogwood (*Cornus foemina* P. Mill.). This small dogwood has brownish twigs with white pith and bluish fruits. Its leaves usually are smooth on both surfaces. It occurs in low, wet forests.

Roundleaf Dogwood (*Cornus rugosa* Lam.). As the name implies, this shrubby dogwood has roundish leaves that are woolly on the undersurface. The greenish twigs have white pith. Berries are pale blue. Roundleaf dogwood grows in dry, rocky forests.

Red-Osier Dogwood (*Cornus sericea* L.). Red-osier dogwood has dark red twigs with white pith. The leaves are pale and somewhat hairy on the undersurface. The berries are white or grayish. Red-osier usually grows along shores, often forming thickets.

Silky Dogwood (*Cornus obliqua* Raf.). This plant is usually a shrub but may grow up to 15 feet tall. It has twigs with pale brown pith. The leaves are pale on the undersurface and usually have white, appressed hairs. The berries are blue. Silky dogwood commonly grows in bottomland forests.

Willow Dogwood (*Cornus amomum* Mill.). Willow dogwood rarely exceeds a height of 10 feet. Like silky dogwood, it has twigs with pale brown pith. The leaves usually have reddish hairs on the undersurface. The berries are pale blue. Willow dogwood commonly grows in bottomland forests.

Other Dogwoods

Gray Dogwood

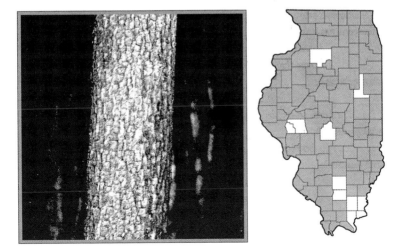

COCKSPUR HAWTHORN
Crataegus crus-galli L.

Growth form: Small tree, up to 20 feet tall; trunk diameter up to 8 inches; crown broadly rounded

Bark: Dark brown, scaly

Twigs: Moderately stout, light brown, smooth, usually with sharp spines up to 4 inches long; leaf scars alternate, crescent-shaped, slightly elevated, with 3 bundle traces

Buds: Rounded, up to $1/4$ inch in diameter, reddish brown, usually smooth

Leaves: Alternate, simple; blades broadest above the middle, rounded or short-pointed at the tip, tapering to the base, up to 4 inches long, up to $1 1/2$ inches broad, leathery, toothed along the edges, at least in the upper one-half of the leaf; dark green, smooth, shiny on the upper surface, paler and smooth on the lower surface; petioles stout, up to 1 inch long, smooth

Flowers: Perfect; showy, several in a cluster, appearing in May and June, each up to $3/4$ inch across, with 5 white petals

Fruit: Pome; spherical or nearly so, up to $1/2$ inch in diameter, red, fleshy but dry, with 1 to 2 nutlets

Wood: Diffuse to semi-ring-porous; heavy, hard, close-grained, brown

Uses: Sometimes grown as an ornamental

Habitat: Wooded slopes, thickets

Range: Native to Illinois; southern Ontario across to Minnesota, south to Texas, east to South Carolina

Distinguishing features: Cockspur hawthorn differs from most other hawthorns in Illinois by its leathery, shiny leaves, which are broadest above the middle.

Cockspur Hawthorn

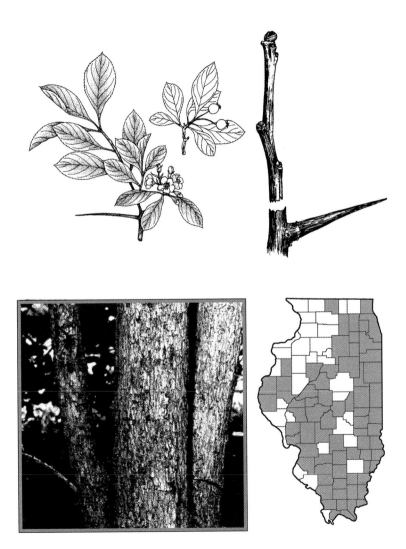

DOWNY HAWTHORN
Crataegus mollis Scheele

Other names: Red hawthorn

Growth form: Small tree, up to 25 feet tall; trunk diameter up to 14 inches; crown
widely spreading

Bark: Gray–brown, scaly, deeply furrowed

Twigs: Moderately stout, gray or brown, smooth or slightly hairy, rarely with spines;
leaf scars alternate, crescent-shaped, slightly elevated, with 3 bundle traces

Buds: Rounded, up to $1/4$ inch in diameter, reddish brown, usually hairy

Leaves: Alternate, simple; blades ovate, broadest near the base, short-pointed at the tip,
rounded at the base, up to 4 inches long and nearly as broad, coarsely toothed along
the edges, occasionally with shallow lobes, yellow–green and hairy on the upper
surface, paler and hairy on the undersurface; petioles stout, up to 1 inch long, hairy

Flowers: Perfect; showy, several in a cluster, appearing in April and May, each up to   1
inch across, with 5 white petals

Fruit: Pome; spherical or nearly so, up to 1 inch in diameter, red, fleshy but dry, with
4 to 5 nutlets

Wood: Diffuse to semi-ring-porous; heavy, hard, close-grained, brown

Uses: Used almost exclusively for ornamental and wildlife plantings; sometimes
firewood

Habitat: Moist forests

Range: Native to Illinois; southern Ontario across to Minnesota, south to Oklahoma,
east to Alabama

Distinguishing features: Downy hawthorn is distinguished by its densely hairy,
ovate leaves, which are often shallowly lobed.

Downy Hawthorn

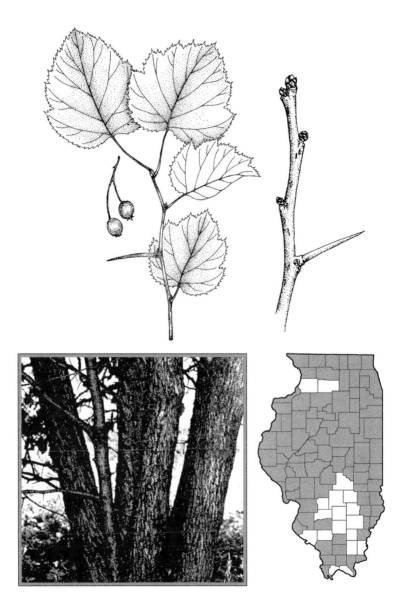

FROSTED HAWTHORN

Crataegus pruinosa (Wendl. f.) K. Koch

Other names: Pruinose hawthorn, waxy-fruit hawthorn

Growth form: Small tree, to 15 feet tall; trunk diameter up to 8 inches; crown broad and irregular

Bark: Dark gray, scaly, furrowed

Twigs: Slender, reddish brown, smooth, with spines up to 2 inches long; leaf scars alternate, crescent-shaped, slightly elevated, with 3 bundle traces

Buds: Rounded, up to $1/8$ inch in diameter, reddish brown, smooth or nearly so

Leaves: Alternate, simple; blades mostly ovate, broadest below the middle, pointed at the tip, rounded at the base, up to 3 inches long and about two-thirds as broad, coarsely toothed along the edges and frequently shallowly lobed, bluish green and smooth on the upper surface, paler and smooth on the undersurface; petioles stout, up to 1 inch long, smooth or somewhat hairy

Flowers: Perfect; showy, several in a cluster, appearing in May and early June, each up to 1 inch across, with 5 white petals

Fruit: Pome; spherical or nearly so, up to $3/4$ inch in diameter, dark red to purple, fleshy but dry, with 5 outlets

Wood: Diffuse to semi-ring-porous; heavy, hard, close-grained, brown

Uses: Used almost exclusively for ornamental and wildlife plantings; sometimes firewood

Habitat: Forests and thickets

Range: Native to Illinois; Newfoundland to southern Ontario, south to Arkansas, east to North Carolina

Distinguishing features: Frosted hawthorn is distinguished by its bluish green leaves, which are widest just below the middle.

Frosted Hawthorn

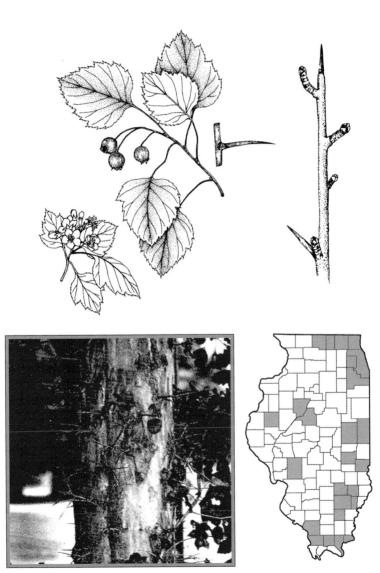

OTHER HAWTHORNS

Many other hawthorns occur in Illinois. Several of them have been found only a few times. Most of them are difficult to distinguish unless leaves, flowers, and fruits are available.

Pear Hawthorn [*Crataegus calpodendron* (Ehrh.) Medik.]. Pear hawthorn (or urn-shaped hawthorn) is named for the shape of its fruit, which is usually about $1/2$ inch long, red, with sweet flesh and 2 to 3 nutlets inside. This small tree grows to a height of only about 15 feet. Leaves are usually ovate, coarsely toothed and often shallowly lobed. They have a greenish yellow color and are hairy, at least on the undersurface. This hawthorn frequently grows along rocky streams.

Kansas Hawthorn (*Crataegus coccinioides* Ashe). This hawthorn grows to a height of 15 feet and has scaly brown bark. The slender gray twigs have many stout, sharp spines up to 2 inches long. Leaves are ovate, coarsely toothed and usually shallowly lobed. There are some hairs on both surfaces of the leaves. The spherical fruits, when mature, are deep red speckled with several pale dots. There are usually five nutlets inside each fruit. The Kansas hawthorn is found primarily on rocky hills.

Dotted Hawthorn (*Crataegus punctata* Jacq.). This hawthorn grows to a height of about 20 feet and has many stout thorns on its twigs. The obovate leaves are generally broadest above the middle. Leaf edges are usually toothed from the middle to the tip. Sometimes lobes are formed. The leaves have a relatively thick texture and are hairy on the veins of the undersurface of the leaves. The usually spherical fruit is about $3/4$ inch in diameter and contains 3 or 5 nutlets. Dotted hawthorn often forms thickets along the edges of forests or in rocky fields.

Green Hawthorn (*Crataegus viridis* L.). Green hawthorn is primarily a tree of low, wet forests, where it grows to a height of nearly 30 feet and has gray, scaly bark. The rather variable leaves range from elliptic to elliptic-ovate and toothed to occasionally shallowly lobed. The leaves are thin and smooth on both surfaces, except for some tufts of hair along the axils of the veins on the undersurface. The orange–red fruits are spherical and about $1/3$ inch in diameter. There are five nutlets embedded in the rather sweet flesh.

Other Hawthorns

Green Hawthorn

Dotted Hawthorn

Pear Hawthorn

COMMON PERSIMMON
Diospyros virginiana L.

Growth form: Medium-sized tree, up to 80 feet tall; trunk diameter up to 2 feet; crown broad and rounded or flattened. At one time in the Wabash Valley, persimmon trees nearly 3 feet in diameter were commonly found.

Bark: Dark gray to black, broken at maturity into squarish blocks

Twigs: Slender, brown, smooth or hairy, usually with lenticels; leaf scars alternate, half-elliptic, with 1 bundle trace

Buds: More or less rounded, smooth, dark reddish brown, up to $1/8$ inch long

Leaves: Alternate, simple; blades elliptic to oval, pointed at the tip, tapering or rounded at the base, up to 5 inches long and about one-half as broad, smooth along the edges, dark green, smooth and shiny on the upper surface, paler and smooth on the lower surface; petioles stout, up to 1 inch long, smooth or sparsely hairy

Flowers: Dioecious; staminate and pistillate usually borne on separate trees, appearing after the leaves are one-half grown; staminate flowers in clusters of 2 to 3, tubular, up to $1/2$ inch long; pistillate flowers solitary, $1/2$ to $3/4$ inch long; sometimes flowers with both stamens and pistils can be found

Fruit: Berry; fleshy, spherical, but with the greenish calyx persistent at one end, yellow–orange to orange (rarely blue), up to 2 inches in diameter, sweet when ripe, few-seeded

Wood: Semi-ring-porous; heavy, hard, heartwood dark brown to black

Uses: Commercial value; lumber, veneer, furniture, pulpwood, railroad crossties, handle stock, crates, boxes, pallets, blocking, bobbins, spools, shuttles, golf club heads, and firewood; fruit edible

Habitat: Moderately well-drained to somewhat poorly drained bottomland forests; attains its best development on deep, fertile, well-drained alluvial soils; also grows in upland forests that range in fertility and moisture

Range: Native to Illinois; Connecticut across to southern Iowa and eastern Kansas, south to eastern Texas, east to Florida

Distinguishing features: The leaves of the common persimmon are most often confused with those of the blackgum, but usually the tip is not as abruptly pointed in common persimmon. The pith of common persimmon twigs also lacks the distinct partitions found in the blackgum.

Common Persimmon

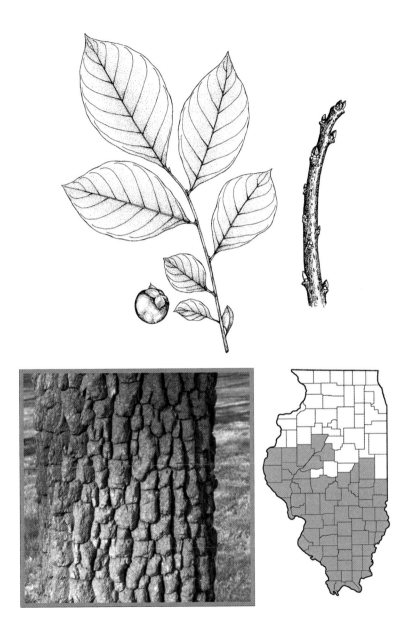

AMERICAN BEECH
Fagus grandifolia Ehrh.

Growth form: Large tree, up to 100 feet tall; trunk diameter up to 4 feet; crown widely spreading, usually rounded

Bark: Smooth, gray, thin, often marred by human carving

Twigs: Gray or yellowish, slender, smooth, somewhat zigzag; leaf scars alternate, half-round, with 3 bundle traces

Buds: Slender, narrow, long-pointed, smooth, reddish brown, up to $3/4$ inch long

Leaves: Alternate, simple; blades up to 4 inches long and $2^1/2$ inches broad, oblong, pointed at the tip, rounded or tapering to the somewhat asymmetrical base, coarsely toothed along the edges, blue–green to yellow–green, smooth and shiny on the upper surface, smooth or finely hairy on the lower surface; petioles very short, sometimes hairy

Flowers: Monoecious; staminate and pistillate borne separately on the same tree, appearing after the leaves have unfolded; staminate flowers numerous in small spherical heads; pistillate flowers in pairs

Fruit: Nut; spiny burs up to $3/4$ inch long, prickly, reddish brown, containing 1 to 3 triangular nuts

Wood: Diffuse-porous; hard, strong, close-grained, light to dark reddish brown

Uses: Commercial value; lumber, veneer, furniture, pulpwood, flooring, railroad crossties, turned products, novelties, food containers, slack cooperage, millwork, crates, boxes, pallets, blocking, and firewood

Habitat: Well-drained to moderately well-drained upland forests; prefers rich, deep, moist upland sites, including coves, low slopes, and ravines; may be found in well-drained bottomland forests

Range: Native to Illinois; Nova Scotia across to Ontario, south to eastern Texas, east to northern Florida

Distinguishing features: The stately American beech is recognized by its smooth, gray bark and long, pointed winter buds.

American Beech

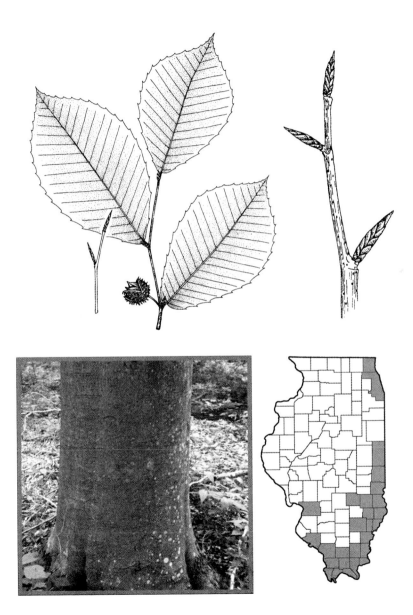

SWAMP-PRIVET
Forestiera acuminata (Michx.) Poir.

Growth form: Small tree, up to 30 feet tall; trunk diameter up to 5 inches; crown spreading, irregular

Bark: Brown, shallowly furrowed or nearly smooth

Twigs: Slender, brown, warty or smooth; leaf scars opposite, shield-shaped, with 1 bundle trace

Buds: Spherical, up to $1/8$ inch in diameter, smooth

Leaves: Opposite, simple; blades elliptic, pointed at the tip, tapering to the base, up to 4 inches long, up to $1 1/2$ inches broad, finely toothed along part of the edges, yellow–green and nearly smooth on the upper surface, paler and smooth on the lower surface; petioles slender, usually smooth, up to $1/2$ inch long

Flowers: Dioecious; staminate and pistillate borne separately on different trees, appearing before the leaves begin to unfold; staminate many in rounded clusters, yellow, without petals; pistillate several in branched clusters, yellowish, without petals

Fruit: Drupe; slender, oblong, slightly curved, dark purple, about 1 inch long, up to $1/4$ inch wide, fleshy but dry, containing 1 seed

Uses: Occasionally planted as an ornamental

Habitat: Swamps, along rivers

Range: Native to Illinois; South Carolina across to Kansas, south to Texas, east to Florida

Distinguishing features: Swamp-privet is distinguished by its opposite, pointed leaves, which are finely toothed along the edges.

Swamp-Privet

CAROLINA BUCKTHORN
Frangula caroliniana (Walt.) Gray

Growth form: Small tree, up to 30 feet tall; trunk diameter up to 6 inches; crown spreading

Bark: Gray, somewhat roughened

Twigs: Slender, gray or pale brown, smooth or somewhat hairy; leaf scars alternate, crescent-shaped, with 3 bundle traces

Buds: Lance-shaped, pointed, up to $1/4$ inch long, very hairy

Leaves: Alternate, simple; blades elliptic, short-pointed at the tip, tapering or somewhat rounded at the base, up to 6 inches long, up to 2 inches broad, finely toothed or toothless along the edges, dark green, smooth and glossy on the upper surface, paler and smooth or finely hairy on the undersurface; petioles finely hairy, up to 1 inch long

Flowers: Perfect; few in umbrella-like clusters; inconspicuous, appearing when the leaves are nearly grown, each flower with 5 small petals

Fruit: Drupe; spherical berries, up to $1/3$ inch in diameter, red and shiny, containing 2 to 4 seeds

Wood: Semi-ring to diffuse-porous; hard, lightweight, close-grained, light brown

Uses: Firewood

Habitat: Rocky forests and along streams

Range: Native to Illinois; Virginia across to Kansas, south to Texas, east to Florida

Distinguishing features: Carolina buckthorn is distinguished by its shiny, elliptical leaves; red berries; and small stature.

Carolina Buckthorn

WHITE ASH
Fraxinus americana L.

Growth form: Large tree, up to 100 feet tall; trunk diameter up to 4 feet; crown pyramidal or ovoid, with slender branches; trunk straight, columnar

Bark: Light or dark gray, with diamond-shaped furrows or interlaced ridges; sometimes blocky in appearance

Twigs: Slender, gray or brown, sometimes with a few hairs; leaf scars opposite, crescent-shaped, with several bundle traces forming a half-moon

Buds: Rounded, dark brown, finely hairy, up to $1/2$ inch long

Leaves: Opposite, pinnately compound, with 5 to 9 leaflets; leaflets lance-shaped to lance-ovate, often curved, pointed at the tip, rounded or tapering to the base, up to 5 inches long and about one-half as broad, shallowly toothed along the edges, green and smooth on the upper surface, paler and smooth or hairy on the lower surface; autumn color purplish

Flowers: Dioecious; staminate and pistillate borne on separate trees before the leaves begin to expand, minute, without petals, purplish, in crowded clusters, soon becoming elongated and less crowded

Fruit: Samara; paddle-shaped, winged, up to $2^1/2$ inches long and $1/4$ inch wide, several in a cluster, 1-seeded at the base

Wood: Ring-porous; heavy, strong, hard, coarse-grained, brown to grayish brown

Uses: A valuable timber species; lumber, veneer, furniture, pulpwood, cabinets, flooring, interior finishing, slack cooperage, baseball bats, handle stock, oars, railroad crossties, pallets, blocking, and firewood

Habitat: Well-drained to moderately well-drained upland forests; prefers rich, deep, moist upland sites, including coves, low slopes, and ravines

Range: Native to Illinois; Nova Scotia across to Minnesota, south to Texas and Florida

Distinguishing features: White ash differs from green ash in the following ways: habitat (predominantly an upland species), shape of leaf scar (crescent-shaped), shape of the samara (paddle-shaped), and autumn foliage (purplish).

White Ash

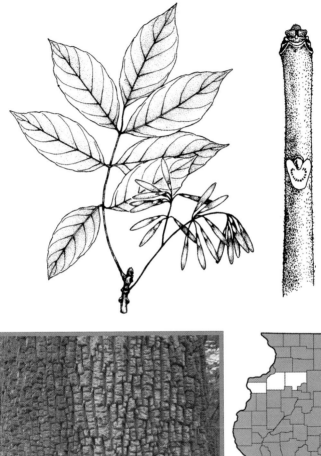

BLACK ASH
Fraxinus nigra Marsh.

Growth form: Medium-sized tree, up to 70 feet tall; trunk diameter up to 2 feet; crown broadly rounded, with many stout, straight branches

Bark: Light gray, scaly, without diamond-shaped furrows

Twigs: Stout, gray or brown, smooth; leaf scars elliptic or oval, with several bundle traces arranged in a half-moon

Buds: Conical, black, finely hairy, about $1/4$ inch long

Leaves: Opposite, pinnately compound, with 7 to 11 leaflets; leaflets without stalks, lance-shaped, long-pointed at the tip, tapering or rounded at the sometimes asymmetrical base, up to 6 inches long, less than one-half as wide, toothed along the edges, dark green and smooth on the upper surface, paler and with rusty hairs along the veins on the lower surface; leaflets turn reddish brown in the autumn

Flowers: Polygamous; small, in elongated clusters, appearing before the leaves begin to unfold, purplish, without any petals; some with both stamens and pistils, others with stamens only, others with pistils only

Fruit: Samara; oblong, winged fruits, barely notched at the tip, up to $1 1/2$ inches long, up to $1/2$ inch broad, with a single seed at the base

Wood: Ring-porous; medium heavy, straight-grained, dark brown

Uses: Commercial value; lumber, veneer, furniture, pulpwood, cabinets, flooring, interior finishing, slack cooperage, baskets, handle stock, oars, pallets, blocking, and firewood

Habitat: Somewhat poorly drained to poorly drained bottomland forests; common to seep communities, swampy areas, and floodplains

Range: Native to Illinois; Newfoundland across to Manitoba, south to Iowa, central Illinois, West Virginia, and Delaware

Distinguishing features: This is the only ash in Illinois with sessile leaflets.

Black Ash

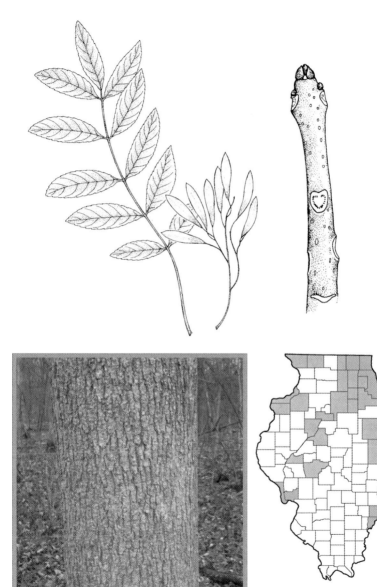

GREEN ASH
Fraxinus pennsylvanica Marsh.

Growth form: Large tree, reaching up to 100 feet tall; trunk diameter up to 3 feet; crown broadly rounded, with slender, spreading branches; rapid growth rate

Bark: Light or dark gray, with diamond-shaped furrows between flattopped, sometimes scaly, ridges

Twigs: Slender to rather stout, gray or brown, smooth; leaf scars half-round (D-shaped) and straight across the top, opposite, with several bundle traces forming   a half-moon

Buds: Rounded, dark brown, finely hairy, up to $1/4$ inch long

Leaves: Opposite, pinnately compound; leaves 10 to 12 inches long with 7 to 9 leaflets; leaflets lance-shaped to elliptic, long-pointed at the tip, tapering to the base, up to 6 inches long and $1^{1}/_2$ inches wide, toothed along the margins, green and smooth on both surfaces; autumn color yellowish orange

Flowers: Dioecious; staminate and pistillate flowers borne on separate trees, in branched clusters, appearing as the leaves begin to unfold; small, purplish, without petals

Fruit: Samara; lance-shaped or reversely lance-shaped, winged fruits, usually rounded at the tip, up to $2^{1}/_2$ inches long and less than $1/3$ inch broad, with a single seed at the base

Wood: Ring-porous; hard, heavy, strong, light brown to grayish brown

Uses: A valuable timber species; lumber, veneer, furniture, pulpwood, cabinets, flooring, interior finishing, slack cooperage, baseball bats, handle stock, oars, railroad crossties, pallets, blocking, and firewood; widely planted as an ornamental

Habitat: Moderately well-drained to somewhat poorly drained bottomland forests; commonly found along the banks of rivers, streams, and ponds; also extends into moist, well-drained upland forests

Range: Native to Illinois; Nova Scotia across to North Dakota, south to Kansas, east to Louisiana and northern Florida

Distinguishing features: Green ash differs from white ash in the following ways: habitat (predominantly a bottomland species), shape of leaf scar (D-shaped), shape of the samara (lance-shaped), and autumn foliage (yellowish orange).

Green Ash

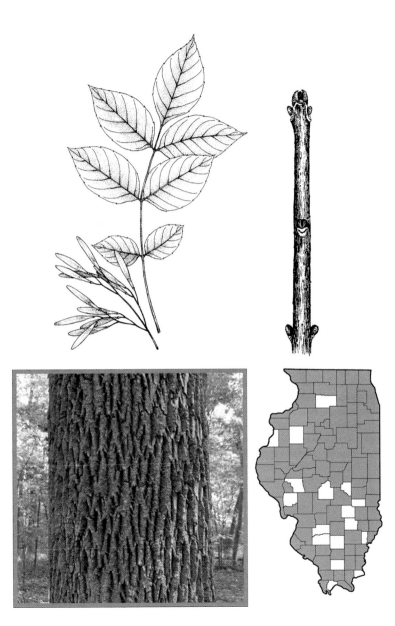

PUMPKIN ASH
Fraxinus profunda (Bush) Bush

Growth form: Large tree, up to 100 feet tall; trunk diameter up to 3 feet; crown broadly rounded, with stout, spreading branches; base of trunk often swollen in wet habitats

Bark: Gray, becoming scaly; also somewhat with an interlacing diamond pattern

Twigs: Stout, gray or brown, usually velvety; leaf scars opposite, crescent-shaped, with several bundle traces arranged in a half-moon; large, conspicuous lenticels

Buds: More or less conical, brown, hairy, about $1/4$ inch long

Leaves: Opposite, pinnately compound, with 7 to 9 leaflets; leaflets lance-shaped to elliptic, pointed at the tip, rounded or tapering at the slightly asymmetrical base, up to 10 inches long and about one-half as wide, smooth or finely toothed along the edges, yellow–green and smooth on the upper surface, paler and velvety-hairy on the lower surface; autumn color yellow

Flowers: Dioecious; staminate and pistillate flowers borne on separate trees, in elongated clusters, appearing before the leaves, small, greenish purple, without any petals

Fruit: Samara; oblong, winged fruits, usually rounded at the tip, up to 3 inches long and $1/2$ inch broad, with a single seed near the bottom

Wood: Ring-porous; heavy, strong, hard, close-grained, brown to grayish brown

Uses: Commercial value; lumber, veneer, furniture, pulpwood, cabinets, flooring, interior finishing, slack cooperage, baseball bats, handle stock, oars, pallets, railroad crossties, blocking, and firewood

Habitat: Somewhat poorly drained to poorly drained bottomland forests and swamps

Range: Native to Illinois; New York across Ohio to southern Illinois and southern Missouri, south to Louisiana, east to Florida

Distinguishing features: Pumpkin ash has larger samaras than all the other native ash species.

Pumpkin Ash

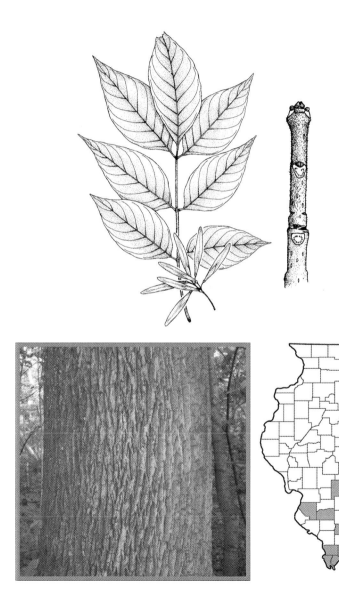

BLUE ASH
Fraxinus quadrangulata Michx.

Growth form: Medium-sized to large tree, up to 100 feet tall; trunk diameter up to 3 feet; crown irregular, with many short, sturdy branches

Bark: Gray, scaly, sometimes with but often without diamond-shaped furrows

Twigs: Stout, 4-angled, gray or brown, smooth; leaf scars half-round and concave across the top, with several bundle traces forming a half-moon

Buds: Rounded, gray, finely hairy, up to $1/2$ inch long

Leaves: Opposite, pinnately compound, with 5 to 11 leaflets; leaflets lance-shaped, long-pointed at the tip, tapering to the sometimes asymmetrical base, up to 6 inches long, less than one-half as wide, coarsely toothed along the edges, yellowish green and smooth on the upper surface, paler and usually with tufts of hairs along the veins on the lower surface; autumn color yellow

Flowers: Perfect; small, in branched clusters, appearing as the leaves begin to unfold, purplish, without any petals; borne on same tree

Fruit: Samara; oblong, winged fruits, notched at the tip, up to 2 inches long and $1/2$ inch broad, with a single seed near the bottom

Wood: Ring-porous; hard, heavy, brown to grayish brown

Uses: A valuable timber species; lumber, veneer, furniture, pulpwood, cabinets, flooring, interior finishing, slack cooperage, baseball bats, handle stock, oars, pallets, railroad crossties, blocking, and firewood

Habitat: Somewhat excessively drained to moderately well-drained upland forests; thrives on high-pH soils of limestone origin; also on slopes extending into bottomland forests

Range: Native to Illinois; Western Pennsylvania across Wisconsin to Iowa, south to Oklahoma, Arkansas, and Alabama; southern Ontario

Distinguishing features: The four-angled stems immediately distinguish this tree from any other ash in Illinois.

Blue Ash

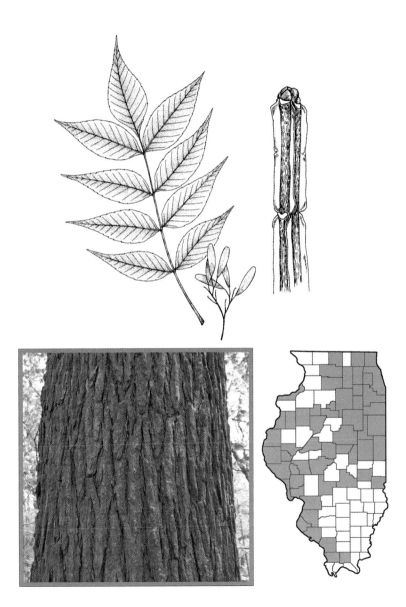

WATERLOCUST
Gleditsia aquatica Marsh.

Growth form: Small to medium-sized tree, up to 60 feet tall; trunk diameter up to 2 feet; crown widely but irregularly spreading; trunk short and stout

Bark: Dark gray or dark brown, shallowly furrowed

Twigs: Slender, gray or brown, smooth, usually with unbranched thorns; leaf scars alternate, more or less 3-lobed, with 3 bundle traces

Buds: Rounded, nearly hidden beneath the leaf scars, dark brown, smooth, up to $1/8$ inch long

Leaves: Alternate, both pinnately and bipinnately compound on the same tree, with many leaflets; leaflets oblong to oblong-ovate, rounded or slightly pointed at the tip, rounded at the slightly asymmetrical base, toothless or minutely toothed along the edges, smooth except for some hairs along the veins, up to 1 inch long, about one-half as wide

Flowers: Polygamo-dioecious; some flowers with both stamens and pistils, others with only 1 or the other, in elongated clusters up to 4 inches long, greenish, small, appearing in May and June

Fruit: Legume; short, pointed pod up to 2 inches long and 1 inch broad, borne several in a drooping cluster, chestnut brown, smooth, with 1 or 2 seeds and no pulp

Wood: Ring-porous; hard, heavy, straight- to irregular-grained, light red to reddish brown

Uses: Limited commercial value; lumber, pulpwood, furniture, interior trim, railroad crossties, fence posts, general construction, pallets, blocking, and firewood

Habitat: Moderately well-drained to poorly drained bottomland forests; a moisture-loving species commonly found near swamps and other bodies of water

Range: Native to Illinois; North Carolina across to southern Missouri, south to Texas, east to Florida

Distinguishing features: The short, one- or two-seeded legume without pulp differentiates waterlocust from honeylocust.

Waterlocust

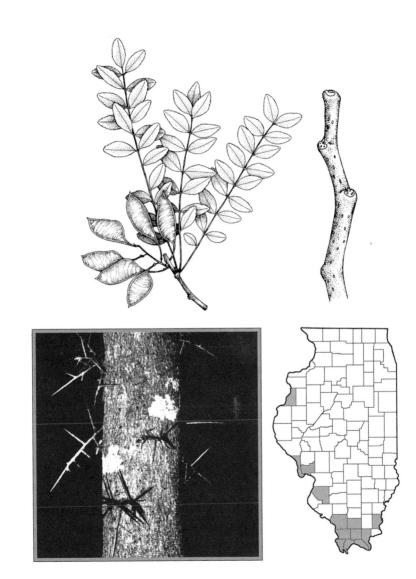

HONEYLOCUST
Gleditsia triacanthos L.

Growth form: Medium-sized to large tree, up to 80 feet tall; trunk diameter up to 3 feet; crown broadly rounded, often with dropping outer branches; trunk straight, rather stout, usually with large, purple–brown, 3-parted thorns

Bark: Dark brown, deeply furrowed and scaly at maturity; often covered in spines

Twigs: Slender, angular, reddish brown, smooth, zigzag, with 3-parted or unbranched thorns; leaf scars alternate, more or less 3-lobed, with 3 bundle traces

Buds: Rounded, nearly hidden beneath the leaf scars, dark brown, smooth, up to $1/8$ inch long

Leaves: Alternate, often bipinnately compound, with many leaflets; leaflets oblong to oblong-lanceolate, rounded or slightly pointed at the tip, rounded at the slightly asymmetrical base, minutely toothed along the edges, smooth except for some hairs along the veins, up to $1^1/2$ inches long, less than one-half as wide

Flowers: Polygamo-dioecious; some flowers with both stamens and pistils, others with only one or the other, in elongated clusters up to 3 inches long, yellowish, small, appearing in May and June

Fruit: Legume; elongated pod up to $1^1/2$ feet long and up to 2 inches wide, flat, often twisted or curved, purple–brown, containing several seeds embedded in a thick pulp

Wood: Ring-porous; hard, strong, straight to irregular-grained, light red to reddish brown

Uses: Commercial value; lumber, pulpwood, furniture, cabinets, interior trim, railroad crossties, fence posts, general construction, pallets, blocking, and firewood

Habitat: A bottomland-adapted species preferring rich, deep, moist soils; also tolerates dry upland sites; commonly found in degraded woodlands with a history of extensive pasturing and lack of forest management

Range: Native to Illinois; New York across to South Dakota, south to Texas, east to Florida

Distinguishing features: Honeylocust has more leaflets than any other kind of tree in Illinois. The large three-parted spines and long fruits also are distinctive, but not all honeylocust trees have spines.

Honeylocust

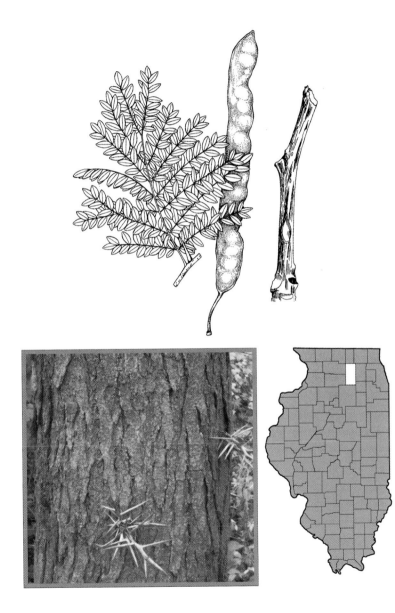

KENTUCKY COFFEETREE
Gymnocladus dioicus (L.) K. Koch

Growth form: Medium to large tree, up to 100 feet tall; trunk diameter up to 3 feet; crown with a narrow, rounded top; trunk stout, usually branching a few feet above the ground

Bark: Dark gray; deeply furrowed and scaly at maturity

Twigs: Stout, dark brown with orange lenticels, slightly hairy; leaf scars alternate, heart-shaped, with 3 or 5 bundle traces; pith chocolate-colored

Buds: Tiny, sunken in hairy cavities immediately above each leaf scar

Leaves: Alternate, bipinnately compound, with many leaflets; leaflets ovate, pointed at the tip, rounded at the base, up to 2 inches long and about one-half as broad, without teeth along the edge, dark green and smooth on the upper surface, yellow–green and smooth or hairy on the veins on the lower surface

Flowers: Dioecious; staminate and pistillate borne separately on different trees, in more or less elongated, greenish clusters, appearing after the leaves have unfolded, each flower with 5 oblong, hairy petals

Fruit: Legume; short, thick pods up to 10 inches long and up to 2 inches wide, dark brown, leathery, smooth, containing several large seeds embedded in a thick, sweet pulp

Wood: Ring-porous; heavy, strong, durable, straight-grained, light red or reddish brown (resembling honeylocust)

Uses: Commercial value; lumber, pulpwood, furniture, cabinets, interior trim, railroad crossties, fence posts, general construction, pallets, blocking, and firewood

Habitat: Moderately well-drained to somewhat poorly drained bottomland forests; typically a bottomland species, nevertheless thrives on rich, upland forest sites

Range: Native to Illinois; New York across to South Dakota, south to Oklahoma, east to Tennessee

Distinguishing features: The bipinnately compound leaves with large leaflets, short, thick legumes, and thick twigs with sunken buds readily distinguish this tree. It is one of the last trees to put forth its leaves in the spring. It has the largest leaf of any native hardwood in Illinois.

Kentucky Coffeetree

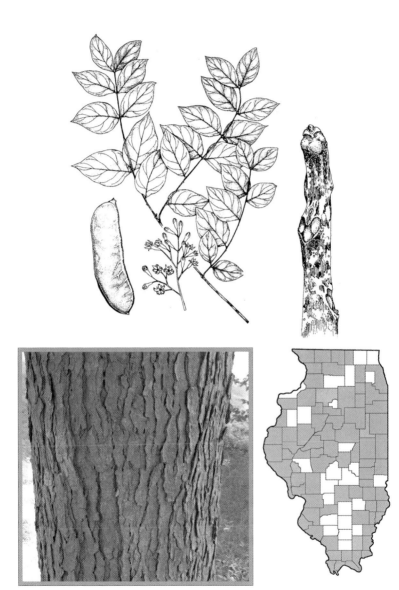

CAROLINA SILVERBELL
Halesia tetraptera Ellis

Other names: Taxonomists disagree regarding the nomenclature and preferred common name of this species. Some refer to Carolina silverbell as *Halesia carolina;* others refer to Carolina silverbell (a.k.a., mountain silverbell or common silverbell) as *Halesia tetraptera.*

Growth form: Small to medium-sized tree, up to 60 feet tall; trunk diameter up to $1^1/2$ feet; crown widely spreading

Bark: Reddish brown, with whitish stripes, somewhat scaly

Twigs: Slender, reddish brown, usually smooth; leaf scars alternate, half-round, with a cluster of bundle scars

Buds: Ovoid, pointed, reddish brown, somewhat hairy, up to $1/8$ inch long

Leaves: Alternate, simple; blades oval to elliptic, pointed at the tip, tapering to rounded at the base, up to 6 inches long, about one-half as broad, finely toothed along the edges, dark green and usually smooth on the upper surface, paler and smooth or slightly hairy on the undersurface; petioles slender, smooth or finely hairy, up to $1/2$ inch long

Flowers: Perfect; few in hanging clusters, showy, white, each bell-shaped and up to 1 inch long, appearing in April

Fruit: Drupe; 4-winged, dry, brown, up to 2 inches long, containing 1 seed

Wood: Diffuse-porous; strong, dense, lightweight, close-grained, pale brown

Uses: Limited commercial value in Illinois; veneer, cabinetwork, wood carvings; occasionally grown as an ornamental

Habitat: Well-drained to moderately well-drained upland forests; prefers rich, deep, moist upland sites, including coves, low slopes, and ravines

Range: Native to Illinois; Virginia across southern Illinois to Oklahoma, south to Texas, east to Florida

Distinguishing features: The bell-shaped white flowers and the four-winged fruits readily distinguish this handsome tree.

Carolina Silverbell

WITCH-HAZEL
Hamamelis virginiana L.

Other names: American witch-hazel

Growth form: Small tree, up to 25 feet tall; trunk diameter up to 10 inches; crown
broadly rounded

Bark: Light brown, eventually broken into small scales

Twigs: Slender, flexible, brown, hairy at first but becoming smooth; leaf scars alternate, half-round, with 3 bundle traces

Buds: Narrow, pointed, finely hairy, orange–brown, up to $1/2$ inch long

Leaves: Alternate, simple; blades obovate, rounded or short-pointed at the tip, rounded
or sometimes tapering to the base, up to 6 inches long, sometimes nearly one-half as
broad, usually with several low, rounded teeth, dark green and usually somewhat
hairy on the upper surface, paler and hairy on the lower surface; petioles up to
$3/4$ inch long, slightly hairy

Flowers: Perfect; blooming from September to November, several in a cluster, each
with 4 bright yellow, strap-shaped petals up to $2/3$ inch long

Fruit: Capsule; up to $1/2$ inch long, brown, hairy, splitting open during the following
autumn to liberate several small, shiny seeds

Wood: Diffuse-porous; medium density, straight-grained, dark brown

Uses: Planted as an ornamental; medicinal uses

Habitat: Forests

Range: Native to Illinois; southern Quebec across to Minnesota, south to Missouri,
Tennessee, and Georgia

Distinguishing features: The late flowering period and the obovate leaves with
shallow, rounded teeth characterize witch-hazel.

Witch-hazel

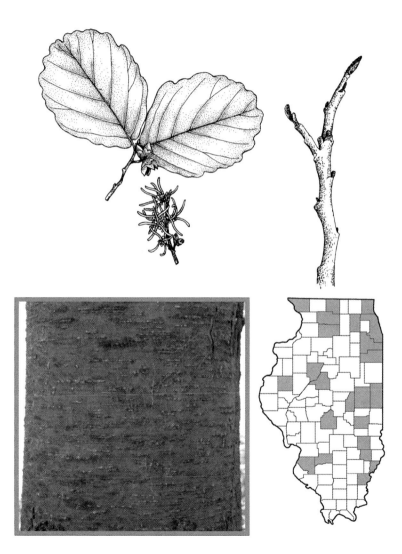

POSSUMHAW
Ilex decidua Walt.

Other names: Swamp holly, deciduous holly

Growth form: Small tree, up to 20 feet tall; trunk diameter up to 3 inches; crown
spreading

Bark: Light brown, more or less warty

Twigs: Slender, gray, smooth or slightly hairy, often with short spurs; leaf scars alternate, crescent-shaped, slightly elevated, with 1 bundle trace

Buds: Rounded, gray, up to $1/8$ inch in diameter

Leaves: Alternate, simple, sometimes clustered at the tips of the short, spurlike twigs;
blades narrowly oblong to elliptic, short-pointed or rounded at the tip, tapering to
the base, up to 3 inches long, less than one-half as broad, sparsely and finely
toothed along the edges, green and smooth on the upper surface, paler and slightly
hairy on the undersurface; petioles slender, hairy, up to $1/4$ inch long

Flowers: Dioecious; staminate and pistillate borne separately on different trees, appearing in April and May; both types of flowers in few-flowered clusters, greenish or
whitish, with usually 4 small petals

Fruit: Drupe; red or rarely orange berries, spherical, up to $1/4$ inch in diameter, remaining on the tree during the winter

Wood: Diffuse-porous; hard, heavy, close-grained, whitish

Uses: Handsome berries make this an attractive ornamental

Habitat: Bottomland forests

Range: Maryland across to eastern Kansas, south to Texas, east to Florida

Distinguishing features: Possumhaw is distinguished by its alternate, remotely toothed
leaves clustered at the ends of spurlike shoots and by its red berries.

Possumhaw

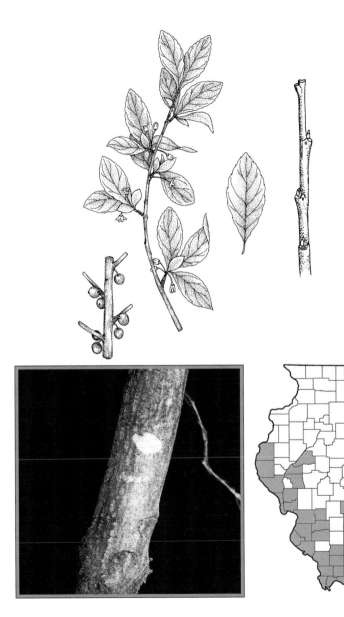

BUTTERNUT
Juglans cinerea L.

Other names: White walnut

Growth form: Medium-sized tree, up to 80 feet tall; trunk diameter up to 3 feet; crown flat to broadly rounded; trunk straight, columnar, not buttressed; increasingly rare due to a canker

Bark: Light gray, divided by deep furrows into broad scaly ridges

Twigs: Stout, greenish or orange–brown to gray, smooth or hairy, usually shiny, with white lenticels; pith chocolate-colored, divided by partitions; leaf scars alternate, shield-shaped, elevated, with 3 bundle traces

Buds: Blunt at the tip, whitish, hairy, soft, up to $1/2$ inch long

Leaves: Alternate, pinnately compound, with up to 17 leaflets; leaflets up to 3 inches long and 2 inches wide, broadly lance-shaped, pointed at the tip, rounded at the asymmetrical base, finely toothed along the edges, yellow–green on the upper surface, paler on the undersurface, softly hairy and sometimes sticky; terminal leaflet usually present

Flowers: Monoecious; borne separately but on the same tree, appearing when the leaves are partly grown; staminate flowers several in thick, yellow–green catkins; pistillate flowers much fewer in spikes; neither of them with petals

Fruit: Nut; in groups of 2 to 5, ovoid-oblong, up to $2^1/2$ inches long, sticky-hairy; husk thick; nut pointed at one end with well-developed wings, pale brown; seed sweet

Wood: Semi-ring-porous; soft, lightweight, coarse-grained, chestnut brown

Uses: Commercial value; quality lumber, face veneer, furniture, pulpwood, cabinets, flooring, wall paneling, interior finishing, turned products, novelties, carvings, and firewood

Habitat: Well-drained to moderately well-drained upland forests; occasionally found on terraced bottomland forest sites with excellent drainage

Range: Native to Illinois; New Brunswick across to Minnesota, south to Arkansas, east to Georgia

Distinguishing features: Butternut is distinguished by its bark pattern; chocolate-colored, partitioned pith; and distinctive fruit.

Butternut

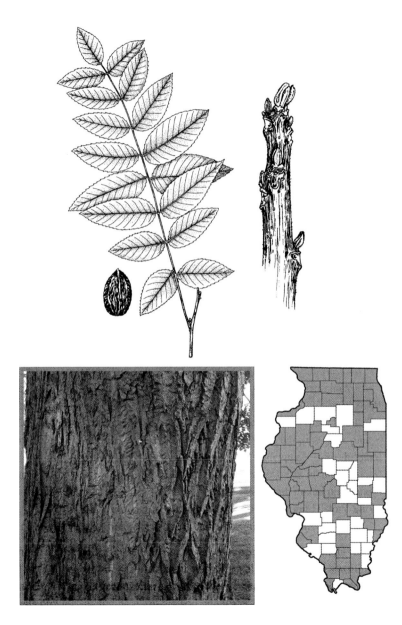

BLACK WALNUT
Juglans nigra L.

Other names: Eastern black walnut

Growth form: Large tree, up to 120 feet tall; trunk diameter up to 5 feet; crown broadly rounded; trunk straight, columnar, not buttressed at the base

Bark: Black, thick, deeply furrowed but sometimes blocky in appearance

Twigs: Stout, greenish or orange–brown, hairy, smooth and gray; pith brown, divided by partitions; leaf scars alternate, shield-shaped, elevated, with 3 bundle traces

Buds: More or less rounded at the tip, pale brown, soft, hairy, up to $1/2$ inch long

Leaves: Alternate, aromatic, pinnately compound, with 15 to 23 leaflets; terminal leaflet usually absent; leaflets up to $3^1/2$ inches long and $1^1/2$ inches wide, broadly lance-shaped, pointed at the tip, rounded at the asymmetrical base, toothed along the edges, yellow–green and smooth on the upper surface, paler and hairy on the lower surface; autumn color yellow

Flowers: Monoecious; borne separately but on the same tree, appearing when the leaves are partly grown; staminate flowers several, in thick, yellow–green, hairy catkins; pistillate flowers much fewer, in small spikes; neither of them with petals

Fruit: Nut; borne singly or in pairs, spherical, up to 2 inches in diameter, green or yellow–green, slightly roughened; husk thick and fragrant; nut very hard, oval, dark brown, deeply ridged; seed sweet

Wood: Semi-ring-porous; hard, heavy, coarse-grained, light brown to chocolate brown

Uses: Illinois's most valuable hardwood species; high-quality lumber, face veneer, furniture, flooring, gunstocks, cabinets, wall paneling, interior finishing, turned products, novelties, carvings, and firewood

Habitat: Moderately well-drained to somewhat poorly drained bottomland forests; attains its best development on deep, fertile, well-drained alluvial soils; also thrives in rich, well-drained upland forests

Range: Massachusetts across to Minnesota, south to Texas, east to Florida

Distinguishing features: Black walnut is recognized by its characteristic buds; light brown, chambered pith; and distinctive fruits. The terminal leaflet is lacking or very small.

Black Walnut

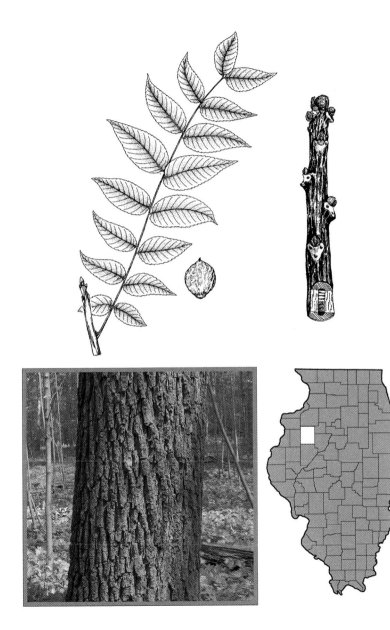

EASTERN REDCEDAR
Juniperus virginiana L.

Other names: Redcedar

Growth form: Small to medium-sized tree, up to 70 feet tall, usually much smaller; trunk diameter up to 3 feet; crown narrowly pyramidal or broad and rounded

Bark: Reddish brown, splitting into long shreds

Twigs: Slender, brown

Leaves: Of two types, either flat, triangular, opposite, and up to $1/16$ inch long; or short and needlelike, up to $3/4$ inch long; blue–green to green to yellow–green

Flowers: Dioecious; staminate and pistillate on different trees; staminate conelets in small, narrow, yellowish spikes; pistillate conelets in small, ovoid, purplish clusters

Fruit: Fleshy seed cone; berrylike, spherical, up to $1/4$ inch in diameter, dark blue with a whitish covering, with sweet flesh and 1 to 2 seeds

Wood: Durable, lightweight, close-grained, fragrant, whitish brown to red

Uses: Commercial value; lumber, pulpwood, furniture, plywood, cabinets, interior trim, fence posts, novelty items, storage chests, closets, millwork, pencils, woodenware, and firewood

Habitat: Excessively drained to well-drained upland forests; commonly found on dry, gravelly ridge tops, slopes, and abandoned fields

Range: Native to Illinois; New Brunswick across to North Dakota, south to Texas, east to Florida

Distinguishing features: The two kinds of leaves readily distinguish this species.

Eastern Redcedar

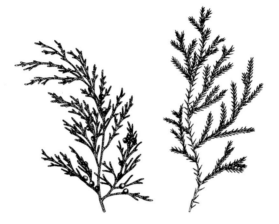

EUROPEAN LARCH
Larix decidua P. Mill.

Growth form: Medium-sized to large tree, up to 80 feet tall; trunk diameter up to 24 inches; crown straight and more or less columnar

Bark: Light brown, scaly

Twigs: Moderately stout, yellowish, with numerous conspicuous leaf scars or, when older, with short lateral spurs

Leaves: Needles borne many in clusters from short spurs or borne singly on new branchlets, soft, yellow–green, up to about 1 inch long, somewhat triangular, falling from the tree in the autumn

Flowers: Monecious; staminate and pistillate borne separately but on the same tree, appearing as the new leaves begin to appear; staminate flowers in nearly round, yellow heads; pistillate flowers in oblong, bright red "cones"

Fruit: Woody cone; oblong, upright, up to $1\frac{1}{4}$ inches long, 30 to 50 scales; containing numerous small, winged seeds

Wood: Hard, lightweight to medium heavy, strong, orange–brown

Uses: Sometimes planted as an ornamental

Habitat: Around homes, where it has persisted from cultivation; plantations

Range: Introduced (from Europe); infrequently escaped from cultivation; often planted as an ornamental due to its larger size and faster growth, as compared to tamarack.

Distinguishing features: European larch differs from tamarack by its larger cones, with more cone scales.

European Larch

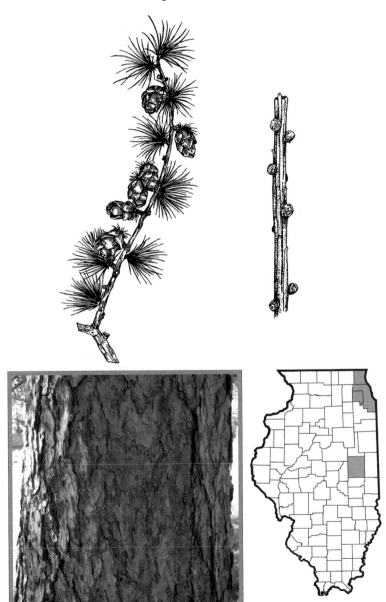

TAMARACK
Larix laricina (Du Roi) K. Koch

Other names: Eastern larch

Growth form: Medium-sized tree, to 60 feet tall; trunk diameter up to $1\frac{1}{2}$ feet; crown narrowly pyramidal

Bark: Reddish brown, broken into scales

Twigs: Slender, light brown or orange, smooth; leaf scars alternate, elevated, borne on spurs, with 1 bundle trace

Buds: Spherical, reddish brown, up to $\frac{1}{8}$ inch in diameter

Leaves: Needles numerous in clusters, soft, up to about 1 inch long, light green, falling away during the autumn

Flowers: Monoecious; staminate spherical, yellow, usually not subtended by leaves; pistillate oblong, rose-colored, usually subtended by leaves

Fruit: Woody cones; oblong, up to $\frac{1}{2}$ inch long, 10 to 20 scales, chestnut brown

Wood: Lightweight to medium heavy, hard, durable, close-grained, orange–brown

Uses: Fence posts, railroad ties, interior finishing; sometimes grown as an ornamental

Habitat: Bogs and swamps

Range: Native to Illinois; Labrador to Alaska, south to Minnesota, northern Illinois, and West Virginia

Distinguishing features: Tamarack is distinguished from European larch by its much smaller woody cones with fewer cone scales.

Tamarack

SWEETGUM
Liquidambar styraciflua L.

Other names: Redgum

Growth form: Large tree, up to 100 feet tall; trunk diameter sometimes more than 3 feet; crown usually pyramidal

Bark: Usually dark gray and broken into scaly ridges

Twigs: Stout, yellow–brown to green, often bordered by corky wings; leaf scars alternate, half-elliptical, slightly elevated, with 3 bundle traces

Buds: Large, shiny, pointed, sometimes sticky to the touch, green and orange–brown in color

Leaves: Alternate, simple; blades shaped like 5- to 7-pointed stars, each point toothed along the edge, as much as 6 inches long and nearly as broad; autumn color ranges from red to yellow to purple

Flowers: Monoecious; staminate and pistillate on same tree, crowded together in rounded clusters, opening at about the same time as the leaves unfold

Fruit: Capsule; dry "ball" about 1 inch in diameter, covered by numerous short, often sharp projections, with many seeds, most of which are incapable of germinating

Wood: Diffuse-porous; hard, strong, durable, reddish brown to brown in color

Uses: Commercial value; lumber, veneer, furniture, pulpwood, cabinets, flooring, interior finishing, millwork, woodenware, slack cooperage, plywood, boxes, baskets, crates, railroad crossties, pallets, blocking, and firewood

Habitat: Moderately well-drained to poorly drained bottomland forests; by preference a bottomland species, however, occupies marginal to rich upland forest sites

Range: Native to Illinois; southwestern Connecticut across southern Illinois to eastern Oklahoma and eastern Texas, east to central Florida

Distinguishing features: The star-shaped leaves and spiny fruit readily distinguish this tree.

Sweetgum

YELLOW-POPLAR
Liriodendron tulipifera L.

Other names: Tulip-poplar, tuliptree

Growth form: Large tree, up to 120 feet tall; trunk diameter up to 4 feet; crown oblong or pyramidal from a long, columnar trunk

Bark: Grayish, becoming deeply furrowed at maturity; furrows often whitish within

Twigs: Smooth, reddish brown; leaf scars alternate, nearly spherical, with several bundle traces, with stipule scars encircling the twig

Buds: Flattened, up to 1 inch long, resembling a duck's bill

Leaves: Alternate, simple; blades divided into 4 broad lobes, the upper 2 lobes usually with a conspicuous notch between them, bright green, averaging 4 to 6 inches long and broad

Flowers: Perfect; about 2 inches long, cup-shaped, with 6 yellow–green petals with an orange base surrounding a cone-shaped cluster of pistils; opening in May

Fruit: Aggregate of samaras; about $2^{1}/_{2}$ inches long, composed of several winged seeds

Wood: Diffuse-porous; soft, durable, yellowish green

Uses: A valuable timber species; lumber, face veneer, rotary veneer, furniture, pulp-wood, plywood (core stock), cabinets, boxes, crates, interior finishing, musical instruments, general construction, pallets, blocking, and firewood

Habitat: Well-drained to moderately well-drained upland forests; prefers rich, deep, moist upland sites, including coves, low slopes, and ravines

Range: Native to Illinois; Connecticut and Vermont across to southern Michigan, southwestward across Illinois to Louisiana, east to Central Florida

Distinguishing features: The shape of the leaf is unlike that of any other tree in Illinois.

Yellow-Poplar

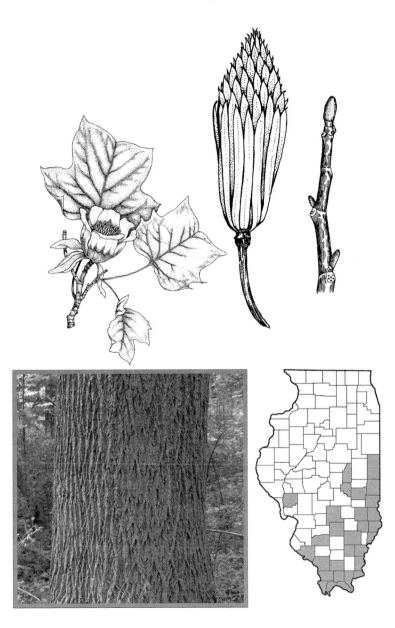

OSAGE-ORANGE
Maclura pomifera (Raf.) Schneid.

Other names: Hedge apple, bowwood, bois d'arc

Growth form: Medium-sized tree, up to 50 feet tall; trunk diameter up to 2 feet; crown rounded or dome-shaped, with several rather stout, spreading branches

Bark: Light gray–brown tinged with orange, separating into shaggy strips

Twigs: Dull orange–brown, smooth, zigzag, with short, sharp, axillary spines; leaf scars alternate, half-round, elevated, with usually 3 groups of bundle traces

Buds: Round, reddish brown, smooth, very tiny

Leaves: Alternate, simple; blades ovate or ovate-lanceolate, long-pointed at the tip, narrowed or a little bit heart-shaped at the base, up to 5 inches long and $3^{1}/2$ inches broad, smooth along the edges, green and smooth on both surfaces; petioles smooth, up to 2 inches long

Flowers: Dioecious; staminate and pistillate borne on separate trees, yellow–green, very tiny; staminate flowers crowded in short clusters on stalks up to 4 inches long; pistillate flowers crowded into spherical heads on short, stout stalks

Fruit: Multiple of drupes; large, spherical, greenish yellow compound fruit up to 6 inches in diameter, containing many seeds, succulent flesh, and milky sap

Wood: Ring-porous; heavy, very hard, flexible, durable, coarse-grained, orange when first cut, becoming darker upon exposure to the elements

Uses: Limited commercial value in Illinois; bows, fence posts, railroad ties, tool handles, and firewood; often planted as a windbreak

Habitat: Moderately well-drained to poorly drained bottomland forests; by preference a bottomland species, however, occupies marginal to rich upland forest sites; commonly found in fencerows adjacent to agricultural fields and degraded woodlands that were heavily pastured

Range: Introduced (from Arkansas, Oklahoma, and Texas); naturalized throughout Illinois

Distinguishing features: Osage-orange is distinguished by its spiny branches; long-pointed, toothless leaves; milky sap; and large, spherical, yellow–green fruits.

Osage-Orange

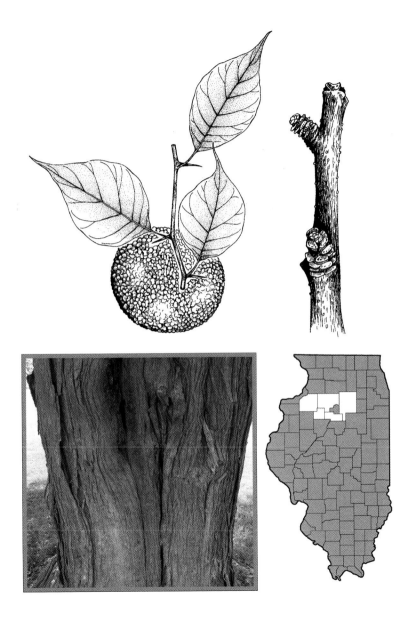

CUCUMBERTREE
Magnolia acuminata (L.) L.

Other names: Cucumber magnolia

Growth form: Medium-sized tree, up to 70 feet tall; trunk diameter up to 2 feet; crown
broadly rounded or pyramidal

Bark: Gray or brown, with shallow furrows when mature

Twigs: Rather stout, reddish brown, smooth; leaf scars alternate, U-shaped, with
several scattered bundle traces

Buds: Silvery white, hairy, up to nearly 1 inch long, with a single bud scale

Leaves: Alternate, simple; blades usually elliptic, short-pointed at the apex, rounded or
tapering to the base, up to 10 inches long and more than one-half as broad, entire
along the edges, yellow–green and smooth on the upper surface, paler and sometimes hairy on the undersurface

Flowers: Perfect; greenish yellow, up to 3 inches long, with usually 6 elongated, pointed petals, appearing in April

Fruit: Aggregate of follicles; oblong fruits up to 3 inches long, deep red, with several
seeds; young fruits look like small cucumbers; ripening from late August to October

Wood: Diffuse-porous; moderately heavy, white to pale brown

Uses: Limited commercial value in Illinois; cabinets, flooring, veneer, furniture, paneling, trim, and framing; planted as an ornamental

Habitat: Well-drained to moderately well-drained upland forests; prefers rich,
deep, moist upland sites, including coves, low slopes, and ravines

Range: Native to Illinois; New York to southern Illinois and Oklahoma, south to
Louisiana and Georgia; also southern Ontario

Distinguishing features: The large, toothless leaves are distinctive from leaves
of all other Illinois trees except the water tupelo, a tree of swamps that usually has
one to three coarse teeth along the edge of each leaf. The silvery buds also are distinctive, as are the flowers and fruits.

Cucumbertree

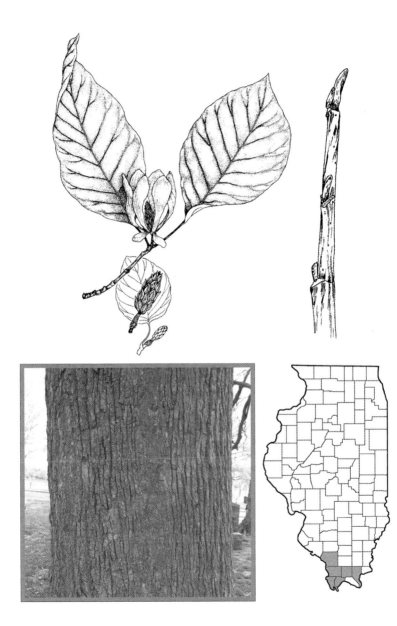

SOUTHERN CRABAPPLE
Malus angustifolia (Ait.) Michx.

Other names: Narrowleaf crabapple

Growth form: Small tree, up to 20 feet tall; trunk diameter up to 9 inches; crown spreading

Bark: Reddish brown, deeply furrowed, scaly

Twigs: Slender, reddish brown or pale brown, smooth, sometimes spurlike; leaf scars alternate, narrow, curved, with 3 bundle traces

Buds: Rounded, brown, up to $1/16$ inch in diameter, finely hairy

Leaves: Alternate, simple; blades elliptic to oblong, rounded or pointed at the tip, narrowed to the base, to 2 inches long, less than one-half as broad, toothed along the edges, seldom shallowly lobed, green and smooth on the upper surface, a little paler and smooth or sparsely hairy on the undersurface; petioles slender, up to 1 inch long, smooth or hairy

Flowers: Perfect; showy, up to 1 inch across, on long stalks, usually 3 or more in a cluster, with 5 narrow, rose-colored petals appearing during May and June

Fruit: Pome; up to 1 inch across, yellow–green, edible

Wood: Diffuse-porous; heavy, close-grained, reddish gray to dark brown

Uses: Firewood and smoking wood; planted as an ornamental

Habitat: Moist forests

Range: Native to Illinois; Maryland across to southern Missouri, south to Louisiana, east to Florida

Distinguishing features: Southern crabapple is distinguished by its narrow, usually unlobed leaves.

Southern Crabapple

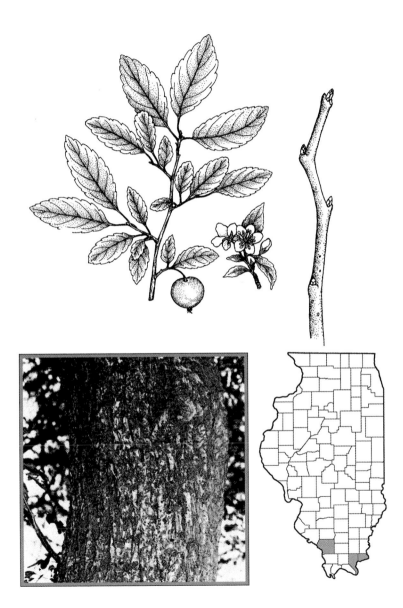

SWEET CRABAPPLE
Malus coronaria (L.) P. Mill.

Growth form: Small tree, up to 25 feet tall; trunk diameter up to 1 foot; crown widely spreading

Bark: Gray–brown to red–brown, with rather deep furrows between the scales

Twigs: Moderately stout, reddish brown, often spurlike, sometimes spiny, usually smooth at maturity; leaf scars alternate, narrow, curved, with 3 bundle traces

Buds: Rounded, reddish, about 1/4 inch in diameter, smooth or nearly so

Leaves: Alternate, simple; blades oval, rounded to short-pointed at the tip, rounded or tapering to the base, up to 3 inches long, about one-half as broad, toothed along the edges and sometimes slightly lobed, yellow–green and smooth on the upper surface, paler on the undersurface; petioles stout, up to 2 inches long, smooth or hairy

Flowers: Perfect; showy, up to 1 1/2 inches across, on long stalks, usually 3 or more in a cluster, with 5 rounded, white or pinkish petals; appearing during May and June

Fruit: Pome; up to 1 inch across, yellow–green, edible

Wood: Diffuse-porous; heavy, close-grained, reddish brown

Uses: Tool handles, smoking wood, and firewood; planted as an ornamental

Habitat: Forests; edge of fields; edge of prairies

Range: Native to Illinois; New York and southern Ontario across to Wisconsin, south to Kansas, Tennessee, and North Carolina

Distinguishing features: Sweet crabapple differs from the southern crabapple by its broader leaves and from the prairie crabapple by its usually less-lobed leaves and smooth flowers.

Sweet Crabapple

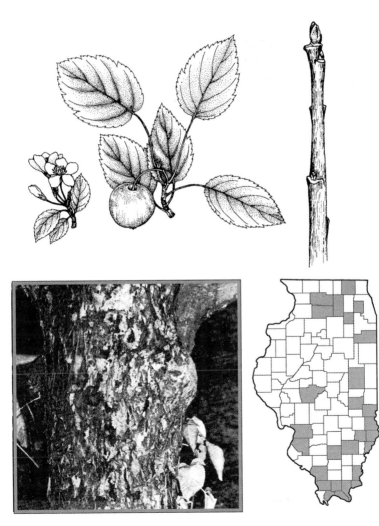

PRAIRIE CRABAPPLE
Malus ioensis (Wood) Britt.

Other names: Iowa crabapple

Growth form: Small tree, up to 25 feet tall; trunk diameter up to 1 foot; crown spreading

Bark: Reddish brown, scaly

Twigs: Moderately stout, reddish brown, sometimes spiny, usually somewhat hairy at maturity; leaf scars alternate, narrow, curved, with 3 bundle traces

Buds: Rounded, reddish brown, less than $1/8$ inch in diameter, finely hairy

Leaves: Alternate, simple; blades elliptic to oval, rounded or pointed at the tip, rounded or tapering to the base, up to $4^1/2$ inches long and less than one-half as broad, toothed along the edges and often shallowly lobed, dark green and smooth on the upper surface, yellow–green and usually somewhat hairy on the undersurface; petioles stout, up to 1 inch long, hairy

Flowers: Perfect; showy, hairy, up to 2 inches across, on long stalks, usually 3 or more in a cluster, with 5 rounded, white or rose petals, appearing during May and June

Fruit: Pome; up to $1^3/4$ inches across, yellow–green, edible

Wood: Diffuse-porous; heavy, close-grained, reddish brown

Uses: Tool handles, smoking wood, and firewood; planted as an ornamental

Habitat: Edges of prairies and fields

Range: Native to Illinois; Wisconsin and Minnesota, south to Nebraska, Texas, and Louisiana

Distinguishing features: Prairie crabapple is distinguished from the other crabapples in the state by the greater frequency of lobed leaves and by its hairy flowers.

Prairie Crabapple

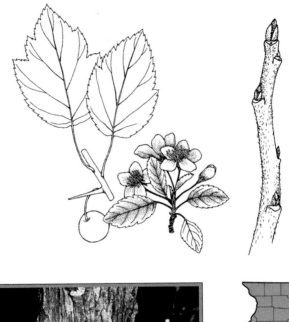

WHITE MULBERRY
Morus alba L.

Growth form: Medium-sized tree, up to 50 feet tall; trunk diameter up to 3 feet; crown broadly rounded, with many short branchlets

Bark: Light brown, sometimes tinted with orange, divided into long, scaly plates

Twigs: Slender, yellowish, smooth or sometimes hairy, more or less zigzag; leaf scars alternate, half-round, elevated, with numerous bundle traces

Buds: Pointed, reddish brown, smooth, about 1/6 inch long

Leaves: Alternate, simple; blades ovate, short-pointed at the tip, rounded or cut straight across at the base, up to 5 inches long and nearly as broad, coarsely round-toothed, sometimes 2-lobed, sometimes 3-lobed, sometimes deeply several-lobed, sometimes unlobed, green and smooth to the touch on the upper surface, paler and smooth on the undersurface except for a few hairs sometimes on the veins; petioles up to 2 inches long, smooth

Flowers: Imperfect, usually dioecious; staminate and pistillate flowers borne separately, either on the same tree or on different trees, appearing as the leaves unfold; staminate flowers crowded into narrow green clusters up to 2 inches long; pistillate flowers crowded into short, thick spikes up to 1 inch long

Fruit: Multiple of drupelets; a cluster of tiny drupes up to 1 1/4 inches long, white or pinkish, more rarely red or purple; sweet, juicy

Wood: Ring-porous; lightweight, soft, coarse-grained, orange–brown to reddish brown

Uses: Fence posts, furniture, wood turning, and firewood; fruit edible

Habitat: Forests, along roads, in disturbed areas, commonly found in fencerows adjacent to agricultural fields and in degraded woodlands that were heavily pastured

Range: Introduced (from Asia); naturalized from Maine to Minnesota, south to Texas, and east to Georgia

Distinguishing features: The leaf surface of white mulberry leaves is typically smoother, greener, and shinier than that of red mulberry. The toothed leaf margins of white mulberry are commonly larger than those of red mulberry. White mulberry fruits are typically found in clusters, whereas red mulberry fruits are usually singular.

White Mulberry

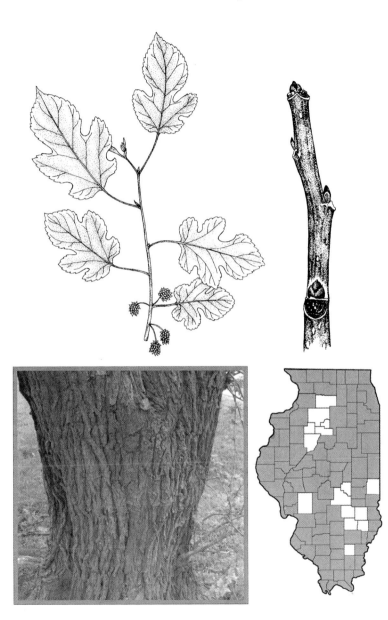

RED MULBERRY
Morus rubra L.

Growth form: Medium-sized tree, up to 70 feet tall; trunk diameter seldom exceeds 2 feet; crown broadly rounded, with many short branchlets

Bark: Dark brown, divided into long, scaly plates

Twigs: Slender, smooth or sometimes hairy, reddish brown to dark brown, more or less zigzag; leaf scars alternate, half-round, elevated, with numerous bundle traces

Buds: Pointed, brown, smooth, up to $1/4$ inch long

Leaves: Alternate, simple; blades mostly ovate, abruptly pointed at the apex, some-what heart-shaped at the base, up to 6 inches long and sometimes nearly as broad, coarsely toothed, sometimes 2-lobed, sometimes 3-lobed, often unlobed; green and usually rough to the touch on the upper surface, paler and with short white hairs on the undersurface; petioles up to $1^1/2$ inches long, smooth at maturity; autumn color yellow

Flowers: Imperfect, usually dioecious; staminate and pistillate flowers borne separately, either on the same tree or on different trees, appearing as the leaves unfold; staminate flowers crowded into narrow, green clusters up to 2 inches long; pistillate flowers crowded into short, thick spikes up to 1 inch long

Fruit: Multiple of drupelets; a cluster of tiny drupes up to $1^1/2$ inches long, at first red, becoming purple or nearly black, rarely remaining pale; sweet, juicy

Wood: Ring-porous; hard, durable, coarse-grained, orange–brown to reddish brown

Uses: Limited commercial value; lumber, pulpwood, fence posts, slack cooperage, agricultural implements, pallets, blocking, and firewood

Habitat: Moderately well-drained to poorly drained bottomland forests; by preference a bottomland species, however, occupies marginal to rich upland forests sites

Range: Native to Illinois; Vermont across to Minnesota and South Dakota, south to Texas, east to Florida

Distinguishing features: Red mulberry buds are usually larger, sitting off-center the twig; and the bud scale margins have a conspicuous black band. Red mulberry is a relatively small-diameter tree, compared to the commonly large diameter of white mulberry.

Red Mulberry

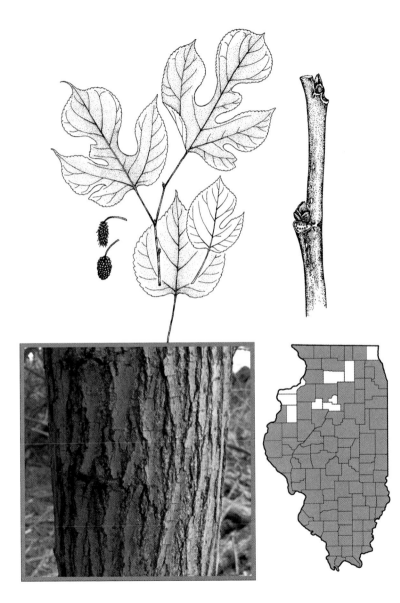

WATER TUPELO
Nyssa aquatica L.

Growth form: Large tree, up to 90 feet tall; trunk diameter up to 3 feet, often swollen at the base; crown spreading, with numerous branchlets

Bark: Light gray to dark gray to brown, broken into thin scales

Twigs: Stout, more or less angular, gray or brown, smooth; leaf scars alternate, broadly U-shaped, with 3 bundle traces

Buds: Rounded, smooth, about 1/8 inch long

Leaves: Alternate, simple; blades oblong to somewhat ovate, pointed at the tip, tapering to rounded to even heart-shaped at the base, up to 8 inches long and about one-half as broad, the edges smooth or with a few coarse teeth, dark green, shiny, smooth or somewhat hairy on the upper surface, paler and soft-hairy on the undersurface; petioles stout, up to 3 inches long, hairy

Flowers: Polygamo-dioecious; staminate and pistillate borne on separate trees, appearing as the leaves begin to unfold, greenish, small; staminate flowers several in spherical clusters; pistillate flowers solitary on long stalks arising from the leaf axils

Fruit: Drupe; fleshy, oblong, dark purple with pale speckles, up to 1 inch long, bitter, 1-seeded, ripening in September

Wood: Diffuse-porous; moderately hard and heavy, interlocked-grain, pale brown to brown

Uses: Commercial value; lumber, furniture, pulpwood, cabinets, woodenware, slack cooperage, boxes, baskets, crates, railroad crossties, pallets, blocking, and firewood

Habitat: Somewhat poorly drained to poorly drained bottomland forests; a moisture-loving species commonly found in swamps

Range: Native to Illinois; Virginia to southern Missouri, south to Texas, east to Florida

Distinguishing features: Water tupelo is characterized by its large, irregularly toothed leaves and its oblong, purple fruits. Water tupelo fruit is larger than that of black-gum.

Water Tupelo

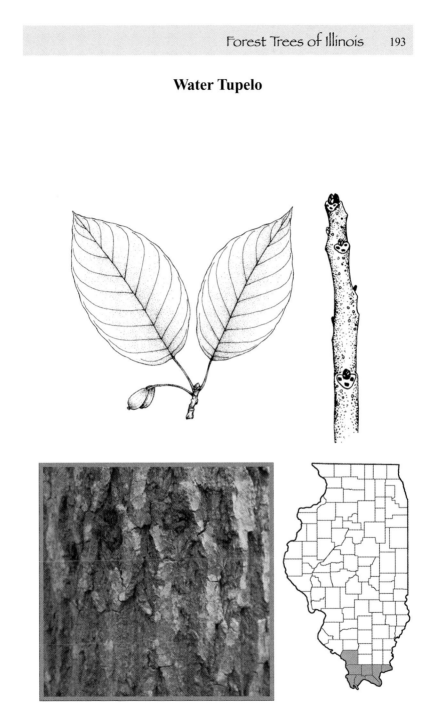

BLACKGUM
Nyssa sylvatica Marsh.

Other names: Black tupelo

Growth form: Medium-sized tree, up to 80 feet tall; trunk diameter up to 3 feet; crown rounded, often with many small, drooping branchlets

Bark: Brown to black, often broken up into squarish blocks

Twigs: Rather stout, reddish brown, smooth, sometimes zigzag; leaf scars alternate, crescent-shaped, with 3 bundle traces; pith continuous but marked with distinct partitions

Buds: Short-pointed, yellowish or reddish, smooth, about $1/8$ inch long

Leaves: Alternate, simple; blades abruptly pointed at the tip, tapering or rounded at the base, up to 6 inches long and usually about one-half as wide, smooth or with a few coarse teeth along the edges, dark green, shiny, and usually smooth on the upper surface, paler and usually somewhat hairy on the undersurface; petioles up to $1^1/2$ inches long, smooth or sparsely hairy; autumn color scarlet

Flowers: Polygamo-dioecious; staminate and pistillate borne on separate trees, appearing after the leaves begin to unfold, greenish, very small; staminate flowers several in spherical clusters; pistillate flowers 2 to several on long stalks arising from the leaf axils

Fruit: Drupe; fleshy, oval, dark blue, up to $1/2$ inch long, bitter, 1-seeded, ripening in October

Wood: Diffuse-porous; moderately hard and heavy, pale brown to brown

Uses: Commercial value; lumber, veneer, furniture, pulpwood, cabinets, woodenware, slack cooperage, boxes, baskets, crates, railroad crossties, pallets, blocking, and firewood

Habitat: A classic generalist; prefers well-drained bottomland forests but thrives in upland forests that range in drainage and fertility

Range: Native to Illinois; Maine across to Michigan and Wisconsin, south to Missouri and Texas, east to Florida

Distinguishing features: Blackgum is easily confused with common persimmon but differs by its leaves, which are abruptly short-pointed at the tip, and its twigs with continuous pith marked by distinct partitions.

Blackgum

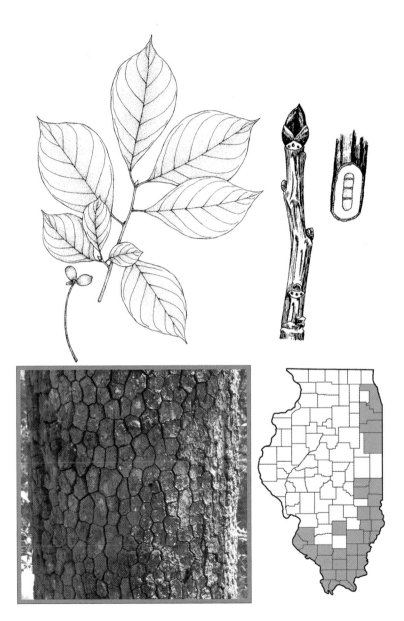

EASTERN HOPHORNBEAM
Ostrya virginiana (P. Mill.) K. Koch

Other names: Ironwood, hophornbeam

Growth form: Small tree, up to 60 feet tall; trunk diameter up to 1 foot; crown usually rounded

Bark: Brown and flaky at maturity

Twigs: Slender, reddish brown, sometimes hairy, tough to break; leaf scars alternate, crescent-shaped, slightly elevated, with 3 bundle traces

Buds: Small, pointed at the tip

Leaves: Alternate, simple; blades elliptic to ovate, pointed at the tip, rounded or tapering to the base, up to 5 inches long, finely doubly toothed, green and usually smooth on the upper surface, paler and usually slightly hairy on the undersurface; petioles up to $1/4$ inch long, hairy

Flowers: Monoecious; staminate and pistillate borne separately but on the same tree; staminate catkins are on the tree through the winter before opening in late April or May

Fruit: Nutlet; enclosed by an inflated bladder, crowded together in a cluster resembling hops

Wood: Diffuse-porous; very heavy and hard, strong, durable, whitish to light brown

Uses: Limited commercial value; tool handles, mallets, fence posts, woodworking, and firewood

Habitat: Somewhat excessively drained to well-drained upland forests; commonly found on rocky ridge tops and dry uplands

Range: Native to Illinois; Nova Scotia across to Manitoba and northeastern Wyoming, south to eastern Texas and northern Florida

Distinguishing features: Eastern hophornbeam and American beech have similar leaves, but the former has flaky bark. Elms, which also have somewhat similar leaves, usually have leaves that are asymmetrical at the base.

Eastern Hophornbeam

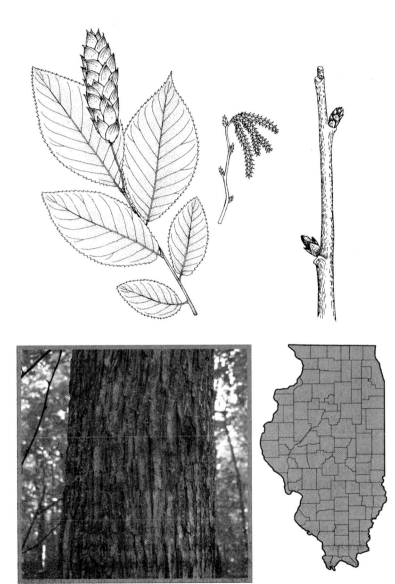

ROYAL PAULOWNIA
Paulownia tomentosa (Thunb.) Sieb. & Zucc. ex Steud.

Other names: Princess tree

Growth form: Small to medium-sized tree, up to 45 feet tall; trunk diameter up to $1^{1}/2$ feet; crown rounded

Bark: Gray, more or less smooth, sometimes lightly ridged

Twigs: Stout, grayish, finely hairy; leaf scars opposite, nearly spherical but with a notch at the top, with many bundle traces in a ring

Buds: True terminal bud lacking; half-round, minutely hairy

Leaves: Opposite, simple; blades mostly heart-shaped, tapering to a short point at the tip, up to about 10 inches long and nearly as broad, smooth along the edges, minutely hairy on both surfaces

Flowers: Perfect; large, showy, fragrant, several in a large cluster, appearing in late April or early May, the clusters sometimes 12 inches long, each flower up to 2 inches long, the petals violet with yellow stripes

Fruit: Capsule; ovoid capsules up to $1^{1}/2$ inches long, pointed at the tip, brown, containing numerous winged seeds

Uses: High-value international markets; popular as an ornamental because of its beautiful flowers; at times invasive in the eastern United States

Habitat: Along roads, around home sites

Range: Introduced (from Asia); naturalized throughout much of the eastern United States, considered to be invasive in many eastern and southern states

Distinguishing features: The leaves of royal paulownia resemble those of the catalpa, but they are always opposite and never in whorls. The violet flowers and short, ovid capsules further distinguish royal paulownia.

Royal Paulownia

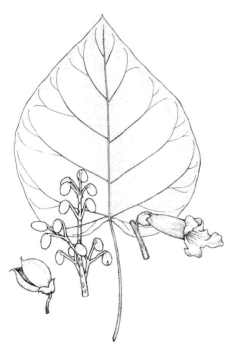

JACK PINE
Pinus banksiana Lamb.

Growth form: Medium-sized tree, up to 75 feet tall in some parts of the United States; trunk diameter up to $2^1/2$ feet; crown open but often irregular

Bark: Reddish brown, rough and scaly

Twigs: Slender, dark brown, becoming roughened

Leaves: Needles in clusters of 2, stiff, curved, up to $1^1/2$ inches long, dark green

Flowers: Monoecious; staminate crowded into several yellow spikes up to $1/2$ inch long; pistillate crowded into few to several purple clusters

Fruit: Woody cone; oblong, curved, upright, up to 2 inches long, each scale comprising the cone bearing a small curved prickle; seeds triangular, up to $1/12$ inch long, with a wing up to $1/3$ inch long

Wood: Moderately light, somewhat resinous, light brown to orange

Uses: Limited commercial value in Illinois; fence posts, fuel, and pulpwood

Habitat: Excessively drained to well-drained upland forests; common to dry and sandy soils

Range: Native to Illinois; Quebec across to Yukon, south to Minnesota, northern Illinois, and New York; Nova Scotia

Distinguishing features: Jack pine is distinguished by its short, stiff, curved needles in clusters of two and its short, curved cones.

Jack Pine

SHORTLEAF PINE
Pinus echinata P. Mill.

Growth form: Medium-sized tree, up to 80 feet tall; trunk diameter up to 2 feet; crown pyramidal or rounded

Bark: Reddish brown, broken into large plates

Twigs: Slender, reddish brown, becoming shreddy; resinous

Leaves: Needles in clusters of both 2 and 3 on the same tree, flexible, up to 5 inches long, dark green

Flowers: Monoecious; staminate crowded into several pale purple spikes up to $3/4$ inch long; pistillate in groups of 1 to 3, rose-colored

Fruit: Woody cone; 1 to 3 in a group, ovoid, up to $2^1/2$ inches long, each scale comprising the cone often bearing a small sharp prickle on the back; seeds triangular; less than $1/4$ inch long, with an asymmetrical curved wing up to $1/2$ inch long

Wood: Hard, heavy, straight-grained, reddish brown

Uses: Commercial value; interior finishing, pulpwood, construction, lumber, and plywood

Habitat: Excessively drained to well-drained upland forests; common to dry, gravelly and sandy soils

Range: Native to Illinois; southern New York across Pennsylvania and southwest Illinois to Oklahoma, south to Texas, east to northern Florida

Distinguishing features: Shortleaf pine is distinguished by its needles, which may be in clusters of two and three on the same tree.

Shortleaf Pine

RED PINE
Pinus resinosa Soland.

Growth form: Medium-sized tree, up to 80 feet tall; trunk diameter up to 3 feet; crown pyramidal

Bark: Reddish brown, divided irregularly into plates

Twigs: Stout, reddish brown, becoming roughened

Leaves: Needles in clusters of 2, up to 6 inches long, dark green, snap easily

Flowers: Monoecious; staminate crowded into several purple spikes up to $1/2$ inch long; pistillate crowded into fewer scarlet clusters

Fruit: Woody cone; ovoid, mostly straight, up to 2 inches long, each scale comprising the cone without any prickles; seeds triangular, up to $1/8$ inch long, with a wing up to $3/4$ inch long

Wood: Rather hard, moderately heavy, straight-grained, reddish brown

Uses: Commercial value; general construction, pulpwood, cabin logs, framing, and utility poles

Habitat: Excessively drained to well-drained upland forests; common to dry, rocky, and sandy soils

Range: Native to Illinois; Newfoundland across to Manitoba, south to Minnesota, Michigan, Pennsylvania, and New Jersey; also north-central Illinois and West Virginia

Distinguishing features: Red pine is distinguished by its dark green needles usually clustered near the tips of the twigs; needles are brittle and snap when bent.

Red Pine

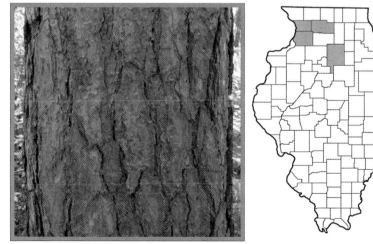

EASTERN WHITE PINE
Pinus strobus L.

Growth form: Large and tall tree, in excess of 150 feet tall in some regions of the United States; trunk diameter sometimes in excess of 3 feet; crown pyramidal

Bark: Brown to dark gray, divided into broad ridges by shallow fissures

Twigs: Slender, orange–brown, smooth or slightly hairy

Leaves: Needles in clusters of 5, very flexible, up to 5 inches long, blue–green

Flowers: Monoecious; staminate crowded into several yellow spikes up to $1/3$ inch long; pistillate crowded into fewer groups; pink to purple

Fruit: Woody cones; oblong, curved, drooping, up to 8 inches long, each scale comprising the cone lacking any prickles; seeds narrowly oblong, up to $1/4$ inch long, with a wing up to $3/4$ inch long

Wood: Lightweight, soft, light brown

Uses: Commercial value; interior finishing, construction, lumber, pulpwood, boxes, furniture, and millwork; planted as an ornamental in windbreaks and for Christmas trees

Habitat: Somewhat excessively drained to moderately well-drained upland forests; prefers rich upland soils but thrives on a variety of sites receiving adequate sunlight; grows poorly on heavy clay soils

Range: Native to Illinois; Newfoundland across to Manitoba, south to Iowa, northern Illinois; in the Appalachian Mountains to northern Georgia

Distinguishing features: The soft, blue–green needles in clusters of five readily distinguish the eastern white pine.

Eastern White Pine

SCOTCH PINE
Pinus sylvestris L.

Other names: Scots pine

Growth form: Medium-sized tree, up to 65 feet tall; trunk diameter up to 2 feet; crown irregular, and commonly forked top

Bark: Reddish brown, broken into plates; bark near top of tree very orange and flaky

Twigs: Slender, brown, roughened

Leaves: Needles in clusters of 2, stiff, up to 3 inches long, gray–green

Flowers: Monoecious; staminate crowded into several yellow spikes up to $1/2$ inch long; pistillate crowded into 1 to several clusters

Fruit: Woody cones; narrowly ovoid, to $2^1/2$ inches long, each scale comprising the cone without any prickles

Uses: Often planted as an ornamental or for Christmas trees; pulpwood

Habitat: Planted in plantations in Illinois, rarely escaped

Range: Introduced (from Europe and Asia); widely planted in the eastern United States

Distinguishing features: The rather short, stiff, gray–green needles in clusters of two distinguish this pine. Bark near top of the tree is orange.

Scotch Pine

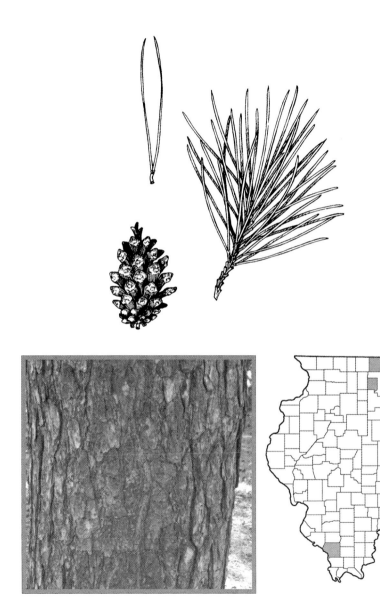

LOBLOLLY PINE
Pinus taeda L.

Growth form: Large tree, sometimes more than 125 feet tall; trunk diameter up to 2 feet; crown rounded

Bark: Reddish brown, divided into irregular plates

Twigs: Slender, brown, becoming roughened

Leaves: Needles in clusters of 3 (or occasionally 2), stiff, up to 9 inches long, light green

Flowers: Monoecious; staminate crowded into several yellow spikes up to $1/2$ inch long; pistillate crowded into 1 to several yellow clusters

Fruit: Woody cone; ovoid to oblong, mostly straight, up to 6 inches long, each scale comprising the cone with a short, sharp prickle; seeds rounded, up to $1/4$ inch long, with a wing up to 1 inch long

Wood: Heavy, strong, straight-grained, reddish brown

Uses: Pulpwood, dimensional lumber, plywood

Habitat: Planted in plantations in Illinois, rarely escaped

Range: Introduced (from the southern and eastern United States); native from New Jersey to Tennessee, south across Arkansas to eastern Texas, east to central Florida

Distinguishing features: Loblolly pine is distinguished by its stiff, long needles (usually in clusters of three) and by its long cones. It is similar to shortleaf pine but has longer needles and cones.

Loblolly Pine

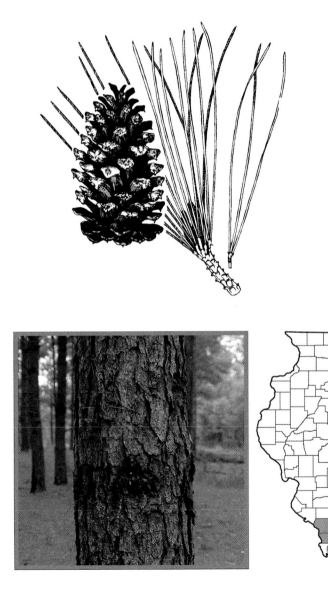

WATER-ELM
Planera aquatica J. F. Gmel.

Other names: Planertree

Growth form: Small tree, up to 30 feet tall; trunk diameter up to 10 inches; crown broadly rounded, with slender branchlets

Bark: Gray or pale brown, smooth at first but later splitting into large scales

Twigs: Slender, reddish brown to gray, usually smooth; leaf scars alternate, nearly circular, each with 3 bundle traces

Buds: Slender, pointed, brownish, smooth or somewhat hairy, up to $1/4$ inch long

Leaves: Alternate, simple; blades lance-ovate, rounded or somewhat pointed at the tip, tapering to the usually asymmetrical base, up to 3 inches long, less than one-half as broad, regularly coarsely toothed, smooth or a little roughened on the upper surface at maturity, smooth or hairy on the undersurface; petioles up to $1/2$ inch long, finely hairy

Flowers: Polygamo-monoecious; of 3 kinds, all on the same tree, appearing after the leaves have begun to expand, greenish yellow, without petals; staminate flowers in several small clusters; pistillate and perfect flowers in drooping clusters of 1 to 3

Fruit: Drupe; oblong, fleshy, up to $1/2$ inch long, with warts (projections) irregularly scattered over the surface, pale brown

Wood: Diffuse-porous to semi-ring-porous; moderately hard, light-weight, close-grained, pale brown

Uses: No commercial value; fence posts and firewood

Habitat: Somewhat poorly drained to poorly drained bottomland forests; prefers deep, rich, moist soils but more often found bordering swamps, ponds, etc.

Range: Native to Illinois; North Carolina across southern Illinois to southeastern Missouri, south to Texas, east to Florida

Distinguishing features: Water-elm resembles other native elms in Illinois but has only single-toothed leaves. The warty fruits also are distinctive.

Water-Elm

SYCAMORE
Platanus occidentalis L.

Growth form: Large tree, sometimes more than 120 feet tall; trunk diameter up to 8 feet; crown broad, often irregular

Bark: Reddish brown when young; quickly breaking into thin, flat scales; sloughing away in sections to expose large patches of whitish or greenish inner bark

Twigs: Smooth, light brown, somewhat zigzag; leaf scars alternate, encircling the buds, somewhat elevated, with 5 to 7 bundle traces

Buds: Light brown, pointed, about 1/4 inch long, entirely covered by the base of the petiole; leaf scar surrounds the base of each bud

Leaves: Alternate, simple; blades circular in outline but divided into 3 or 5 shallow, sharp-pointed lobes, heart-shaped or cut straight across at the base, up to 7 inches long (longer on vigorous shoots) and often as broad, bright green and smooth on the upper surface, paler and smooth on the undersurface except for the sparsely hairy veins; petioles to 5 inches long, slightly hairy; stipules resemble the leaves but only about 1 inch long, often persist near the base of the petioles

Flowers: Monoecious; staminate and pistillate flowers borne separately but on the same tree, minute, crowded together in dense, round heads

Fruit: Achene; round light brown heads, about 1 inch in diameter; on long, drooping stalks; containing many small seeds surrounded by hairs

Wood: Diffuse-porous; moderately hard and strong, light brown

Uses: Commercial value; lumber, veneer, furniture, pulpwood, woodenware, butcher's block, slack cooperage, flooring, food containers, boxes, baskets, crates, railroad crossties, pallets, blocking, and firewood

Habitat: Moderately well-drained to somewhat poorly drained bottomland forests; attains its best development on deep, fertile, well-drained alluvial soils

Range: Native to Illinois; Maine across southern Wisconsin to eastern Nebraska, south to eastern Texas, east to northern Florida

Distinguishing features: The large, palmately lobed leaves and the brown and gray mottled bark readily distinguish this tree.

Sycamore

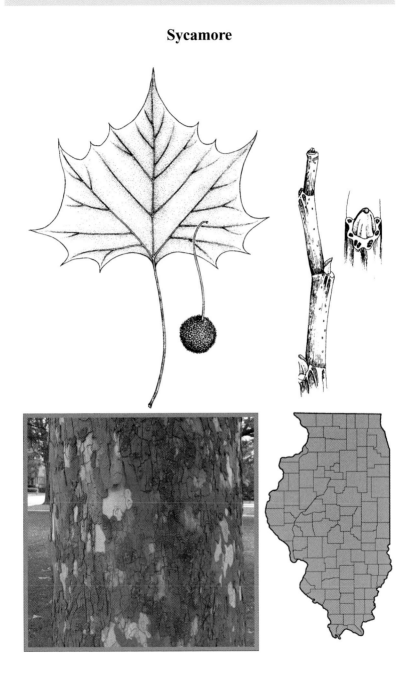

WHITE POPLAR
Populus alba L.

Growth form: Medium-sized tree up to 60 feet tall; trunk diameter up to 2 feet; crown broadly rounded but often irregular

Bark: Grayish to whitish, at first smooth, later becoming deeply fissured and very dark gray to nearly black

Twigs: Greenish gray, white-hairy at least when young; leaf scars alternate, crescent-shaped, each with 3 bundle traces

Buds: Ovoid, pointed, hairy, up to $1/8$ inch long

Leaves: Alternate, simple; blades usually ovate, with a few broad teeth along the edges, bluntly pointed at the tip, cut straight across or a little heart-shaped at the base, up to 4 inches long, dark green on the upper surface, silvery-hairy or white-wooly on the undersurface; petioles up to 3 inches long, densely hairy, not flat

Flowers: Dioecious; staminate and pistillate borne on separate trees, crowded together in catkins, appearing when the leaves unfold

Fruit: Capsule; often curved, flask-shaped, greenish, hairy, up to $1/4$ inch long, containing many seeds with cottony hairs attached

Wood: Diffuse-porous; lightweight, soft

Uses: Grown as an ornamental because of its silvery leaves; invasive

Habitat: Along roads, around old homesteads

Range: Introduced (from Europe and Asia); naturalized throughout Illinois and is often considered an invasive species

Distinguishing features: The leaves, with their silvery or white-wooly undersurface and their few broad teeth, provide the best means of identifying this tree.

White Poplar

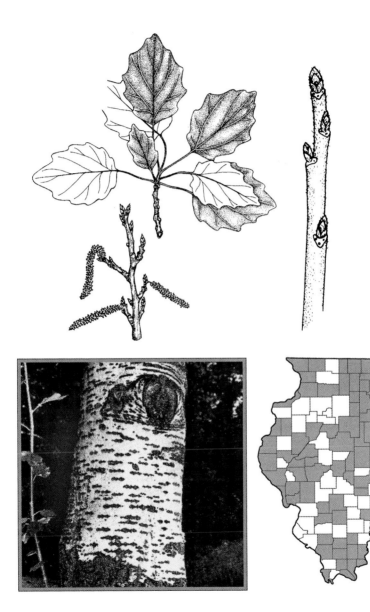

BALSAM POPLAR
Populus balsamifera L.

Growth form: Medium-sized tree, up to 70 feet tall with a long, cylindrical bole; trunk diameter up to 2 feet; crown narrow, pyramidal; upright branches; fast-growing

Bark: Smooth, greenish gray with lighter lenticels when young; eventually becoming gray to grayish-black and dividing into flat, scaly or shaggy ridges separated by narrow, V-shaped fissures

Twigs: Moderately stout, round, shiny, reddish brown to dark brown, with orange lenticels; bitter aspirin taste

Buds: Reddish brown to brown, 1 inch long, curved, sticky, resinous, strongly aromatic in spring

Leaves: Alternate, simple; ovate, or broadly lanceolate; 3 to 6 inches long and $1^1/2$ to 3 inches wide; finely serrated margin and sharply pointed tip, shiny dark green above and pale green below, often marked with fragrant, rust-colored blotches; petioles slender, round, 2 to $3^1/2$ inches long; autumn color yellow

Flowers: Dioecious; male and female as hanging, long, pale yellow–green catkins (2 to $3^1/2$ inches long) appearing in early spring

Fruit: Capsule; small, $^1/4$ to $^1/3$ inch long, ovoid, glabrous, 2-valved dry capsule containing numerous small seeds

Wood: Diffuse-porous; lightweight, soft, light brown to brown

Uses: Limited commercial value in Illinois; pulpwood, lumber, veneer for the manufacture of plywood and paneling (corestock), high-grade paper, waferboard, particleboard, boxes, crates, brackets, carving, interior furniture parts, wooden ware, agricultural implements, and musical instruments

Habitat: Occurs on sites relatively rich in nutrients with low acidity; prefers alluvial soils near rivers, streams, lowland swamps, stream banks, floodplains, sandbars, and lake shores

Range: Native to Illinois; Northeastern counties of Illinois; northernmost-occurring of all North American hardwoods; extends across Canada and into Alaska; east North Dakota, northeast South Dakota, Minnesota, Wisconsin, northwest Indiana, Michigan, southern Ontario, New York, and Maine; local in the western mountains, south to northeast Oregon, Idaho, extreme northern Utah, central Colorado, extreme northwest Nebraska, and the Black Hills of South Dakota and Wyoming; scattered in northern Iowa, northeast Ohio, Pennsylvania, northern West Virginia, extreme eastern Maryland, and northwestern Connecticut

Distinguishing features: Balsam poplar leaves are longer and narrower than quaking aspen, and its fruit is 2-valved.

Balsam Poplar

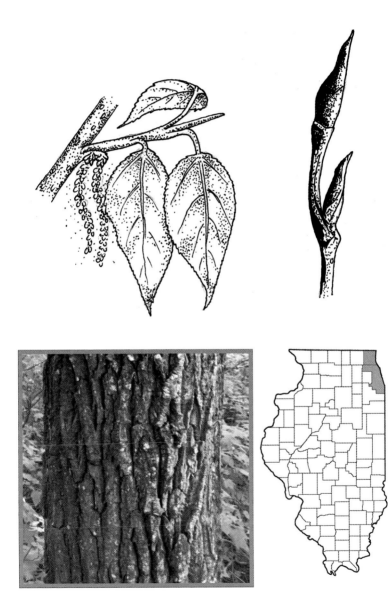

EASTERN COTTONWOOD
Populus deltoides Bartr. ex Marsh.

Growth form: Large, rapidly growing tree, up to 100 feet tall; trunk diameter up to 6 feet; crown spreading or broadly rounded, with some drooping branches

Bark: Smooth and gray when young, becoming furrowed at maturity

Twigs: Yellow–green, gray, or tan; smooth, moderately stout, with numerous pale "dots"; leaf scars alternate, triangular, with 3 large bundle traces

Buds: Lance-shaped, long-pointed, up to $1/2$ inch long, sticky, chestnut-colored

Leaves: Alternate, simple; blades to 5 inches long and often nearly as broad, triangular, abruptly pointed at the tip, cut straight across or even slightly heart-shaped at the base, with coarse, rounded teeth along the edges; green, smooth, and shiny on the upper surface, paler on the undersurface; petioles to 4 inches long, smooth, often yellow, flat

Flowers: Dioecious; staminate and pistillate borne on separate trees; staminate flowers crowded in rather thick, reddish catkins; pistillate flowers crowded in narrower, greenish yellow catkins; both sexes appearing before the leaves begin to unfold

Fruit: Capsule; elliptic, greenish brown, up to $1/4$ inch long, grouped in elongated clusters, containing numerous seeds with cottony hairs attached

Wood: Diffuse-porous; lightweight, soft, readily warping, light brown to brown

Uses: Commercial value; lumber, veneer (core stock), furniture, pulpwood, boxes, baskets, crates, pallets, blocking, and firewood

Habitat: Moderately well-drained to poorly drained bottomland forests; attains its best development on deep, fertile, well-drained alluvial soils

Range: Native to Illinois; New Hampshire across to southeastern North Dakota, south-central Texas, east to northern Florida

Distinguishing features: Eastern cottonwood is easily recognized by its triangular (deltoid) leaves with flattened petioles. The cottony seeds, when the fruits are mature, also are distinctive.

Eastern Cottonwood

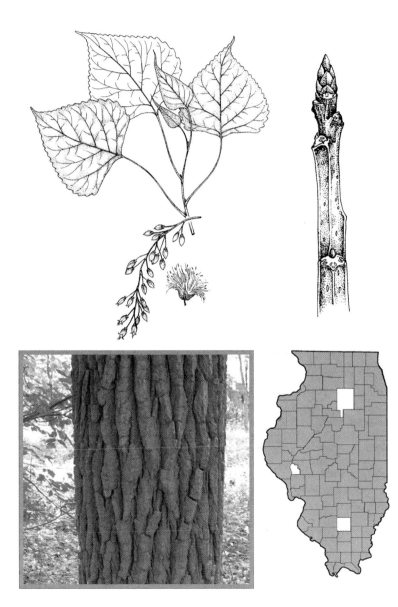

BIGTOOTH ASPEN
Populus grandidentata Michx.

Growth form: Medium-sized tree, up to 80 feet tall; trunk diameter up to $1^{1}/2$ feet; crown rounded

Bark: Grayish green, smooth at first, becoming shallowly fissured and broken up into thin scales

Twigs: Grayish green, with numerous orange "dots," hairy when young but becoming smooth; leaf scars alternate, raised, 3-lobed, each with 3 bundle traces

Buds: Ovoid, pointed, chestnut brown, somewhat hairy, up to $1/8$ inch long

Leaves: Alternate, simple; blades nearly circular in outline, short-pointed at the tip, rounded at the base, up to 5 inches long, nearly as broad, with several rather coarse teeth along the edges, green on the upper surface, paler on the undersurface, smooth when mature; petioles up to 3 inches long, flat, enabling the leaf to rustle even in gentle breezes

Flowers: Dioecious; staminate and pistillate borne on separate trees, crowded together in catkins up to 5 inches long, appearing as the leaves unfold

Fruit: Capsule; long, narrow, flask-shaped, green, slightly hairy, grouped in elongated clusters, containing many seeds with cottony hairs attached

Wood: Diffuse-porous; lightweight, soft, pale brown

Uses: Commercial value; lumber, veneer (core stock), furniture, pulpwood, boxes, baskets, crates, pallets, blocking, and firewood

Habitat: Somewhat excessively drained to moderately well-drained upland forests; commonly found on dry, poor, disturbed upland soils

Range: Native to Illinois; Quebec across to Manitoba, south to central Illinois, east to Maryland; Kentucky and north-central Tennessee east to western North Carolina

Distinguishing features: The coarsely toothed, tremoring leaves and the grayish green bark combine to make this tree easy to recognize.

Bigtooth Aspen

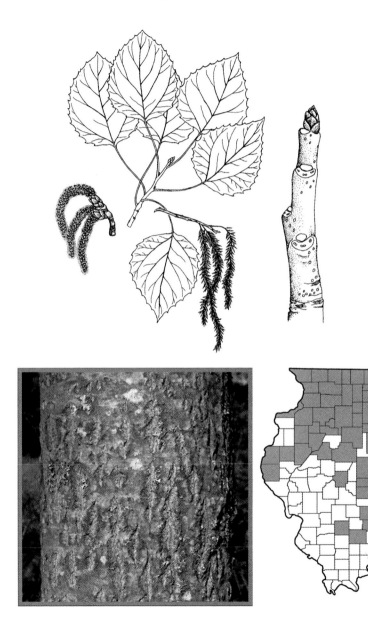

SWAMP COTTONWOOD
Populus heterophylla L.

Other names: Swamp poplar

Growth form: Medium-sized to large tree, up to 90 feet tall; trunk diameter up to 3 feet; crown very irregular, with a few, large, upright branches

Bark: Gray or brown, smooth when young, becoming scaly ridged at maturity

Twigs: Rather stout, smooth or hairy, reddish; leaf scars alternate, 3-lobed, each with 3 bundle traces; pith 5-angled

Buds: Ovoid, pointed, dark brown, sticky, up to $1/2$ inch long

Leaves: Alternate, simple; blades ovate, rounded or bluntly pointed at the tip, heart-shaped at the base, up to 8 inches long, up to 6 inches broad, with rounded teeth along the edges, green on the upper surface, paler on the undersurface, densely white-woolly when young, becoming essentially smooth at maturity; petioles to 4 inches long, smooth or sparsely hairy, not flattened

Flowers: Dioecious; staminate and pistillate borne on separate trees, both appearing before the leaves begin to unfold; staminate flowers crowded in thick catkins up to 4 inches long; pistillate flowers in slender catkins up to 6 inches long

Fruit: Capsule; ovoid, reddish brown, up to $1/2$ inch long, grouped in elongated clusters, containing numerous seeds with cottony hairs attached

Wood: Diffuse-porous; lightweight, soft, pale brown

Uses: Commercial value; lumber, veneer (core stock), furniture, pulpwood, boxes, baskets, crates, pallets, blocking, and firewood

Habitat: Somewhat poorly drained to poorly drained bottomland forests; a moisture-loving species commonly found in low, swampy environments

Range: Native to Illinois; Connecticut to southern Michigan, southwestward across southern Illinois to central Louisiana, east to northern Florida

Distinguishing features: The broad, heart-shaped, toothed leaves readily distinguish the swamp cottonwood from other trees in Illinois.

Swamp Cottonwood

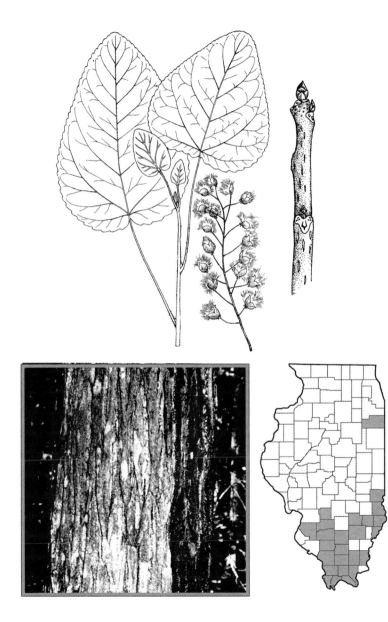

QUAKING ASPEN
Populus tremuloides Michx.

Growth form: Medium-sized tree up to 60 feet tall; trunk diameter up to 1½ feet; crown rounded or occasionally spreading

Bark: Pale yellow–green or white, becoming dark gray to white and divided into dark scaly ridges at maturity

Twigs: Pale yellow–green or white, slender, smooth; leaf scars alternate, crescent-shaped, each with 3 bundle traces

Buds: Lance-shaped, short-pointed, smooth, sticky, up to $1/3$ inch long

Leaves: Alternate, simple; blades ovate to nearly round, short-pointed at the apex, rounded at the base, up to 4 inches long, nearly as broad, with many small round teeth along the edges, green, smooth, and shiny on the upper surface, not shiny on the undersurface; petioles to 3 inches long, smooth, flat; flat petioles allow for the leaves to tremor at the slightest wind

Flowers: Dioecious; staminate and pistillate borne on separate trees; staminate flowers crowded in catkins up to 4 inches long; pistillate flowers crowded in catkins up to 6 inches long

Fruit: Capsule; narrow, flask-shaped, green, up to $1/4$ inch long, grouped in elongated clusters, containing numerous seeds with cottony hairs attached

Wood: Diffuse-porous; lightweight, soft, pale brown

Uses: Limited commercial value in Illinois; lumber, veneer (core stock), furniture, pulpwood, matches, boxes, baskets, crates, pallets, blocking, excelsior, and firewood

Habitat: Favorable to a wide variety of forested sites; pioneer species after disturbance

Range: Native to Illinois; Newfoundland to Alaska; south to California, New Mexico, and Texas; east across Missouri and Tennessee to New Jersey

Distinguishing features: The whitish trunk and the ovate, trembling leaves distinguish this species.

Quaking Aspen

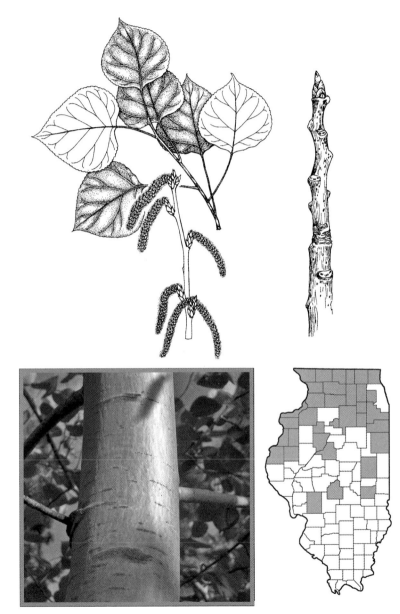

AMERICAN PLUM
Prunus americana Marsh.

Other names: Wild plum

Growth form: Small tree, up to 20 feet tall; trunk diameter up to 8 inches; crown broad, often irregular

Bark: Dark gray to brown, rough and scaly

Twigs: Slender, brown, speckled with many dots, smooth or hairy; leaf scars alternate, half-round, elevated, with 3 bundle traces

Buds: Ovoid, pointed, reddish brown, smooth or hairy, up to $1/4$ inch long

Leaves: Alternate, simple; blades oval to ovate, pointed at the tip, rounded or tapering to the base, up to 4 inches long and less than one-half as broad, finely toothed along the edges, the teeth not glandular, green and smooth or hairy on the upper surface, paler and smooth or hairy on the undersurface; petioles slender, up to 1 inch long, sometimes with 1 or 2 glands near the upper end, smooth or hairy

Flowers: Perfect; showy, several in a cluster, up to 1 inch across, with 5 white or pink-ish petals, appearing before or as the leaves begin to unfold

Fruit: Drupe; spherical or nearly so, up to 1 inch in diameter; red or covered with a whitish wax; juicy, sweet, 1-seeded

Wood: Semi-ring-porous; hard, close-grained, brown

Uses: Fruits used in jelly and preserves; firewood; planted as an ornamental

Habitat: Forests, thickets, and forest edges

Range: Native to Illinois; southern Ontario to Manitoba, south to New Mexico, east to Florida

Distinguishing features: American plum differs from other plums in Illinois by the absence of glands on the teeth of the leaves. The American plum may have either smooth or hairy leaves and twigs.

American Plum

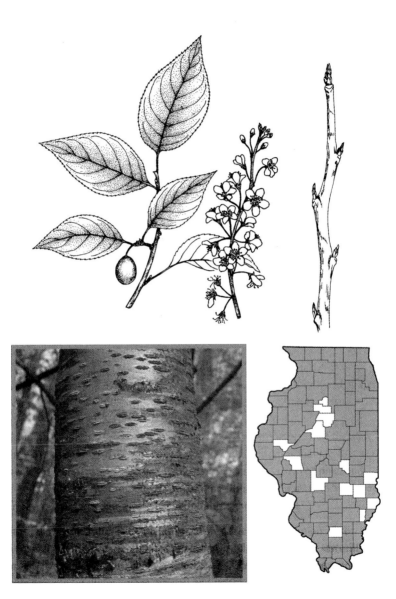

HORTULAN PLUM
Prunus hortulana Bailey

Other names: Wildgoose Plum

Growth form: Small tree, up to 20 feet tall; trunk diameter up to 8 inches; crown broad and rounded

Bark: Gray or brown, becoming scaly at maturity

Twigs: Slender, reddish brown, smooth; leaf scars alternate, half-round, elevated, with 3 bundle traces

Buds: Ovoid, rounded at the tip, reddish brown, smooth, up to $1/4$ inch long

Leaves: Alternate, simple; blades oblong to oval, pointed at the tip, rounded or tapering to the base, up to 6 inches long and about one-third as broad, finely toothed along the edge; the teeth gland-tipped, green and usually smooth on the upper surface, paler and sometimes hairy on the undersurface; petioles slender, up to 1 inch long, with 1 to several glands, smooth or sparsely hairy

Flowers: Perfect, showy, several in a cluster, up to 1 inch across, with 5 white petals, appearing after the leaves are partly grown

Fruit: Drupe; spherical or nearly so, up to 1 inch in diameter, red or rarely yellowish; fleshy but hard; bitter, 1-seeded

Wood: Semi-ring-porous; hard, close-grained, brown

Uses: Fruits used in jelly and preserves; ornamental

Habitat: Edges of forests, thickets

Range: Native to Illinois; Indiana to Iowa, south to Oklahoma, east to Alabama

Distinguishing features: Hortulan plum flowers when its leaves are partly grown, thereby distinguishing it from the American plum, which blooms before or   as the leaves begin to unfold.

Hortulan Plum

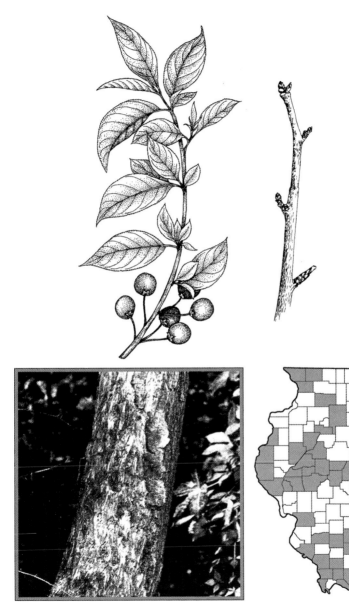

OTHER WILD PLUMS

Two other wild plums are occasionally encountered in Illinois.

Chickasaw Plum (*Prunus angustifolia* Marsh.), also known as narrowleaf plum, is a small tree, up to about 15 feet tall, usually forming thickets. The smooth, brownish twigs usually have several sharp spines. Most of the leaves are lance-shaped and up to 2 inches long, and conspicuously folded lengthwise. The flowers begin to bloom just as the leaves start to unfold. The red, nearly spherical plum has tart, juicy flesh. Chickasaw plum is found mostly in the southeastern United States.

Wildgoose Plum (*Prunus munsoniana* W. Wight & Hedrick), also known as Munsons plum, is a small tree, rarely more than 15 feet tall and often forming thickets. It has gray or brown scaly bark; smooth brownish twigs; and small, ovoid buds. The leaves are oval and up to 6 inches long and up to 2 inches wide. The edges of the leaves are finely toothed, with each tooth gland-tipped. The upper surface of the leaf is smooth, while the lower surface usually has some hairs. The showy white flowers appear while the leaves are developing. The fruits are spherical or slightly oblong red plums with sweet, juicy flesh. Wildgoose plum is found only in the midwestern states.

Wildgoose Plum

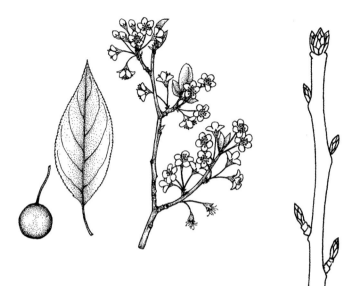

BLACK CHERRY
Prunus serotina Ehrh.

Other names: Wild black cherry

Growth form: Medium-sized tree, up to 80 feet tall; trunk diameter up to 3 feet; crown rounded, with rigid branches

Bark: Thin, smooth, reddish brown at first, becoming deeply furrowed and black

Twigs: Slender, smooth, dark brown; leaf scars half-round, each with 3 bundle traces

Buds: Ovoid, sharp-pointed, dark brown, smooth, up to 1/4 inch long

Leaves: Alternate, simple; blades oblong or oval, short-pointed at the tip, tapering to the base, up to 6 inches long and about a one-third as broad, finely toothed along the edges; green, smooth, and shiny on the upper surface; paler and smooth on the undersurface except for rusty hairs along the veins; petioles slender, slightly less than 1 inch long, smooth, with 1 or more reddish glands near the tip; wilted leaves poisonous because of the prussic acid they contain

Flowers: Perfect; crowded in showy, drooping, elongated clusters up to 6 inches long, appearing when the leaves are partly grown, each flower about 1/4 inch across, with 5 white petals

Fruit: Drupe; fleshy, juicy, spherical, dark purple, up to 1/2 inch in diameter

Wood: Semi-ring-porous; medium density, strong, straight-grained, light reddish brown

Uses: A prized timber species; high-quality lumber, face veneer, high-quality furniture, flooring, cabinets, wall paneling, interior finishing, woodenware, novelties, and firewood

Habitat: Somewhat excessively drained to moderately well-drained upland forests; best development occurs on rich, deep, moist upland sites including coves, low slopes and ravines

Range: Native to Illinois; Nova Scotia across to Ontario, south to Texas, east to Florida

Distinguishing features: Black cherry is similar to chokecherry but usually is a larger tree with thicker leaves, tending to curve inward, and rusty hairs along midrib on underside of leaves.

Black Cherry

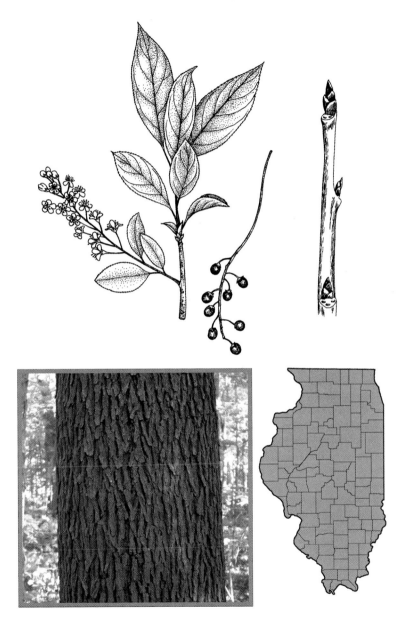

CHOKECHERRY
Prunus virginiana L.

Growth form: Small tree, up to 20 feet tall, often only a shrub; trunk diameter up to 5 inches; crown irregular

Bark: Thin, smooth, and reddish brown at first, becoming furrowed and darkened

Twigs: Slender, smooth, reddish brown with pale lenticels; leaf scars alternate, half-round, each with 3 bundle traces

Buds: Ovoid, pointed, brown, more or less smooth, up to $1/4$ inch long

Leaves: Alternate, simple; blades oblong or oval, short-pointed at the tip, tapering to the base, up to 4 inches long and about one-half as broad, finely and sharply toothed along the edges; green, smooth, and shiny on the upper surface; paler and smooth or with a few hairs on the undersurface; petioles slender, up to 1 inch long, smooth, with 2 glands near the tip

Flowers: Perfect; crowded in showy, drooping, elongated clusters up to 6 inches long, appearing when the leaves are partly grown, each flower up to $1/2$ inch across, with 5 white petals

Fruit: Drupe; fleshy, juicy, spherical, up to $1/3$ inch in diameter, red at first, becoming deep purple at maturity

Wood: Semi-ring-porous; heavy, hard, not strong, close-grained, pale brown

Uses: Limited commercial value; some interior finishing and firewood; ornamental

Habitat: Forests, along streams

Range: Native to Illinois; Newfoundland across to Saskatchewan, south to Kansas, east to North Carolina

Distinguishing features: Chokecherry differs from black cherry by its more pointed teeth along the edges of the leaves and a lack of rusty hairs along the veins on the underside of the leaves.

Chokecherry

COMMON HOPTREE
Ptelea trifoliata L.

Other names: Wafer-ash

Growth form: Small tree or shrub, up to 20 feet tall; trunk diameter up to 5 inches; crown rounded

Bark: Brown, somewhat roughened, aromatic

Twigs: Slender, dark brown, often with small "warts"; leaf scars alternate, large, horseshoe-shaped, slightly elevated, with 3 bundle traces

Buds: Spherical, pale brown, hairy; true terminal bud lacking

Leaves: Alternate, palmately trifoliate; divided into 3 leaflets; leaflets mostly ovate, long-pointed at the tip, rounded or tapering to the base, up to 5 inches long, up to one-half as wide, smooth or with fine teeth along the edges; dark green and smooth on the upper surface, paler and smooth on the undersurface; leaflets sessile

Flowers: Polygamo-monoecious; staminate and pistillate flowers borne separately but usually in the same cluster, appearing in late May and June, with 3 to 5 obscure, greenish white petals

Fruit: Waferlike samara; round, thin, flat, nearly spherical winged seed up to 1 inch across

Wood: Hard, heavy, close-grained, yellow–brown

Uses: Fruit once used as a substitute for hops in brewing

Habitat: Forest edges

Range: Native to Illinois; Quebec across Michigan to Iowa, south to eastern Texas, east to Florida

Distinguishing features: Common hoptree is distinguished by its three-parted alternate leaves and its flat, spherical, winged seeds.

Common Hoptree

WHITE OAK
Quercus alba L.

Growth form: Large tree, up to 100 feet tall; trunk diameter up to 4 feet; crown very broad, with stiff, horizontal branches; trunk relatively short and rather thick

Bark: Gray or whitish with gray patches, shallowly furrowed

Twigs: Slender, smooth, somewhat shiny, gray, whitish or even purplish; pith star-shaped in cross section; leaf scars alternate but crowded near the tip of the twig, half-round, slightly elevated, with several bundle traces

Buds: Nearly round, reddish brown or gray, up to $1/8$ inch long

Leaves: Alternate, simple; blades usually with 7 to 9 lobes, the lobes rounded and not bristle-tipped, the sinuses varying from shallow to deep, the upper surface green and smooth, the lower surface paler and smooth, up to 10 inches long, up to one-half as wide, turning red in the autumn; petioles up to 1 inch long, rather stout, smooth; leaves on the same tree may vary considerably

Flowers: Monoecious; staminate and pistillate borne separately but on the same tree, appearing when the leaves begin to unfold, minute, without petals; staminate flowers many in drooping, yellow catkins; pistillate flowers few in a group, red in color

Fruit: Nut; acorns borne 1 or 2 together, with or without a stalk; nut oblong, up to $3/4$ inch long, green to greenish brown, shiny; cup covering up to one-fourth of the nut, yellow–brown, often minutely hairy; matures first growing season

Wood: Ring-porous; heavy, hard, strong, durable, coarse-grained, light to dark brown

Uses: A prized timber species; high-quality lumber, face veneer, furniture, pulpwood, cabinets, flooring, paneling, interior finishing, railroad crossties, tight cooperage (whisky and wine barrels), general construction, novelties, boxes, crates, blocking, pallets, and firewood

Habitat: Somewhat excessively drained to moderately well-drained upland forests; best development occurs on rich, deep, moist upland sites including coves, low slopes, and ravines

Range: Native to Illinois; Maine across to Minnesota, south to eastern Texas, east to northern Florida

Distinguishing features: White oak is recognized by its grayish bark and 7 to 9 round-lobed, smooth leaves which are usually whitish on the lower surface. Its oblong, greenish brown, shiny acorns also are distinctive.

White Oak

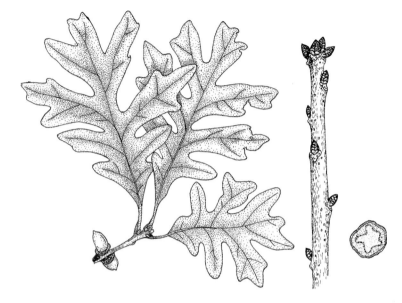

SWAMP WHITE OAK
Quercus bicolor Willd.

Growth form: Large tree, up to 100 feet tall; trunk diameter up to 4 feet; crown rounded and broad

Bark: Grayish brown, deeply furrowed, becoming flaky

Twigs: Stout, grayish brown to yellowish brown; leaf scars alternate, half-round, slightly elevated, with several bundle traces; pith star-shaped in cross section; older branches with flaking bark

Buds: Clustered at the tips of the twigs, ellipsoid to spherical, up to $1/8$ inch long, yellow–brown, smooth or with a few hairs at the tip

Leaves: Alternate, simple; blades usually broadest above the middle, up to 6 inches long and 4 inches broad, coarsely round-toothed or sometimes with a few shallow lobes, smooth or somewhat hairy on the upper surface, white and softly hairy on the undersurface; petioles nearly 1 inch long, smooth or slightly hairy

Flowers: Monoecious; staminate and pistillate borne separately but on the same tree, appearing when the leaves begin to unfold, minute, without petals; staminate flowers in slender, drooping catkins; pistillate flowers in groups of 2 to 4

Fruit: Nut; acorns in pairs, on stalks 1 inch long or longer; nut ovoid, pale brown, 1 to $1^{1}/_{2}$ inches long, enclosed about one-third its length by the cup; cup thick, light brown, hairy, roughened; matures first growing season

Wood: Ring-porous; hard, heavy, strong, light to dark brown

Uses: A valuable timber species; high-quality lumber, face veneer, furniture, pulpwood, cabinets, flooring, paneling, interior finishing, railroad crossties, tight cooperage, general construction, novelties, boxes, crates, blocking, pallets, and firewood

Habitat: Moderately well-drained to poorly drained bottomland forests; also found on upland flats with perched watertable (flatwoods)

Range: Native to Illinois; Maine and southern Quebec across to southern Minnesota, south to Oklahoma, east to Georgia

Distinguishing features: Swamp white oak is distinguished by its leaves, which are coarsely round-toothed and softly white and hairy on the undersurface and its long-stemmed acorns.

Swamp White Oak

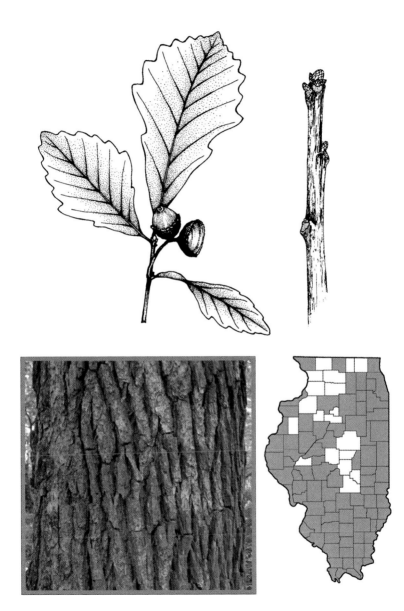

SCARLET OAK
Quercus coccinea Muenchh.

Growth form: Medium-sized tree, up to 70 feet tall in Illinois; trunk diameter up to 2 feet; crown narrow but open

Bark: Reddish brown, shallowly fissured when mature

Twigs: Slender, brown, smooth; leaf scars alternate but crowded near the tip, half-round, slightly elevated, with several bundle traces; pith star-shaped in cross section

Buds: Pointed, reddish brown, hairy at the tip, up to $1/4$ inch long

Leaves: Alternate, simple; blades divided more than half-way to the middle into 5 to 7 bristle-tipped lobes, bright green, shiny and smooth on the upper surface, paler and with tufts of hairs along the veins on the undersurface, up to $6^{1}/2$ inches long and 4 inches broad; petioles up to $2^{1}/2$ inches long, slender, usually smooth

Flowers: Monoecious; staminate and pistillate borne separately but on the same tree, appearing when the leaves begin to unfold, minute, without petals; staminate flowers in slender, drooping catkins; pistillate flowers borne singly or in pairs

Fruit: Nut; acorns solitary or paired, with or without stalks; nut oval or hemispherical, up to $3/4$ inch across, concentric circles often located near the tip, reddish brown with occasional darker rings around it; enclosed up to one-half its length by the cup; cup thin, top-shaped, reddish brown, finely hairy; matures second season

Wood: Ring-porous; hard, heavy, coarse-grained, reddish brown

Uses: Commercial value; high-quality lumber, veneer, furniture, pulpwood, cabinets, flooring, paneling, interior finishing, railroad crossties, slack cooperage, general construction, mine timbers, fence posts, novelties, boxes, crates, blocking, pallets, and firewood

Habitat: Excessively drained to well-drained upland forests; commonly found on dry, gravelly ridge tops, sandy soils, and upland slopes

Range: Native to Illinois; Maine to southern Ontario, south to Oklahoma, east to Georgia

Distinguishing features: Scarlet oak resembles pin oak but differs in habitat and structure of the acorn cup; acorns commonly have concentric circles located near the tip. It sometimes resembles black oak but has shorter, less hairy buds and acorns without loosely arranged scales on the cup.

Scarlet Oak

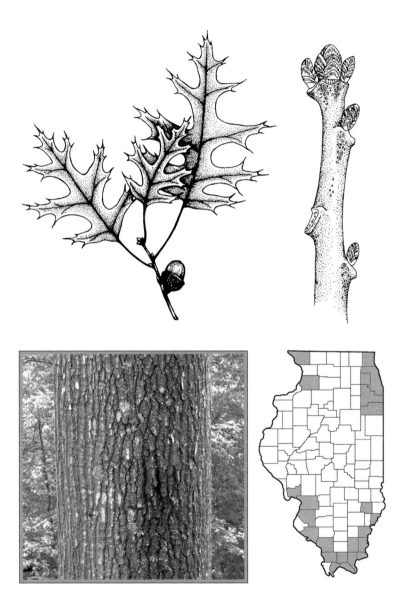

NORTHERN PIN OAK
Quercus ellipsoidalis E. J. Hill

Other names: Hills oak

Growth form: Medium-sized tree, up to 80 feet tall; trunk diameter up to 2 feet; crown rounded, with the drooping lowermost branches often reaching nearly to the ground

Bark: Gray–black, rather smooth to shallowly fissured

Twigs: Rather slender, smooth at maturity, grayish brown to reddish brown; pith star-shaped in cross section; leaf scars alternate but clustered near the tip of the twig, half-round, slightly elevated, with several bundle traces

Buds: Nearly smooth, $1/4$ inch long, ovoid, reddish brown

Leaves: Alternate, simple; blades 3 to 9 inches long, slightly tapering or usually cut nearly straight across at the base, with 2 to 4 pairs of bristle-tipped lobes usually cut over halfway to the midvein, deep green and shiny on the upper surface at maturity; petioles smooth, up to 3 inches long

Flowers: Monoecious; staminate and pistillate on same tree, appearing as the leaves unfold, inconspicuous; staminate flowers crowded in a catkin; pistillate flowers solitary or 2 or 3 together

Fruit: Nut; acorn ripening in October of the second year, on very short stalks; acorns longer than broad, ellipsoidal, short-pointed at the base, about $1/2$ inch across, the cup bowl-shaped covering one-third to one-half of the acorn; matures second season

Wood: Ring-porous; heavy, hard, strong, reddish brown

Uses: Commercial value; high-quality lumber, veneer, furniture, pulpwood, cabinets, flooring, paneling, interior finishing, railroad crossties, slack cooperage, mine timbers, fence posts, novelties, boxes, crates, blocking, pallets, and firewood

Habitat: Somewhat excessively drained to moderately well-drained upland forests; often prefers drier sites

Range: Native to Illinois; northwestern Ohio and central Michigan to southeastern Minnesota, south to eastern Iowa and north-central Illinois

Distinguishing features: The elongated acorn of northern pin oak distinguishes it from pin oak, which it closely resembles.

Northern Pin Oak

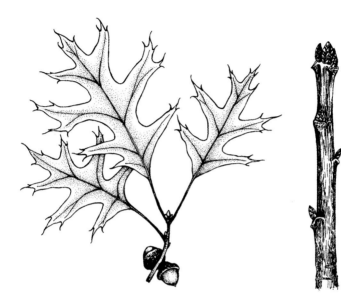

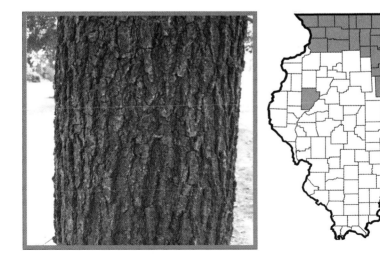

SOUTHERN RED OAK
Quercus falcata Michx.

Other names: Spanish oak

Growth form: Large tree, up to 100 feet tall; trunk diameter up to 4 feet; crown broadly rounded, with stiff, stout, spreading branchlets; trunk straight, rather stout

Bark: Dark brown to nearly black, shallowly furrowed to deeply furrowed

Twigs: Reddish brown to gray, smooth or nearly so at maturity; pith star-shaped in cross section; leaf scars alternate but clustered near the tip, half-round, slightly elevated, with several bundle traces

Buds: Ovoid, pointed, chestnut brown, hairy, up to $1/4$ inch long

Leaves: Alternate, simple; blades broadly rounded at the base, 3- to 5-lobed; the terminal lobe usually long, narrow, and strongly curved; all lobes bristle-tipped, up to 8 inches long, up to 6 inches wide, green on the upper surface, pale and densely soft-hairy on the undersurface; petioles up to $2^{1}/2$ inches long, slender, usually hairy

Flowers: Monoecious; staminate and pistillate borne separately but on the same tree, appearing when the leaves begin to unfold, minute, without petals; staminate flowers in slender, drooping, densely hairy catkins; pistillate flowers few in a rusty-hairy cluster, with dark red stigmas

Fruit: Nut; acorn usually solitary, with or without a short stalk; nut spherical or ellipsoid, up to $1/2$ inch long, orange–brown; cup covering only one-third of the nut, with hairy, reddish brown scales; matures second season

Wood: Ring-porous; heavy, hard, strong, coarse-grained, reddish brown

Uses: A valuable timber species; high-quality lumber, face veneer, furniture, pulpwood, cabinets, flooring, paneling, interior finishing, railroad crossties, slack cooperage, general construction, mine timbers, fence posts, novelties, boxes, crates, blocking, pallets, and firewood

Habitat: Somewhat excessively drained to moderately well-drained upland forests; characteristic of drier, poorer, soils; largest specimens often found on rich, well-drained upland and bottomland sites

Range: Native to Illinois; central New Jersey south to central Florida, across to eastern Texas, up the Mississippi Basin to central Missouri, south-central Illinois, southeastern Indiana, western Kentucky, and western Tennessee

Distinguishing features: Southern red oak has two variable leaf types: a bell-shaped leaf and a turkey-track-shaped leaf.

Southern Red Oak

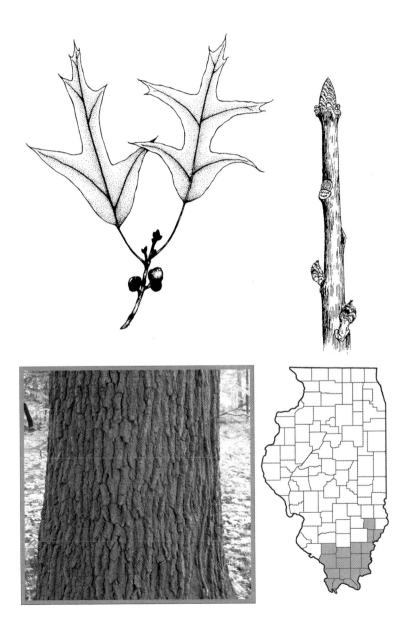

SHINGLE OAK
Quercus imbricaria Michx.

Growth form: Medium-sized to large tree, up to 90 feet tall; trunk diameter up to 3 feet; crown rounded or oblong, with many branches; trunk straight, columnar

Bark: Dark brown, deeply furrowed between flat, tight plates

Twigs: Slender, smooth, reddish brown; pith star-shaped in cross section; leaf scars alternate but crowded near the tip of the twigs, half-round, slightly elevated, with several bundle traces

Buds: Ovoid, pointed, brown, smooth, up to $1/8$ inch long

Leaves: Alternate, simple; blades without lobes or teeth, lanceolate to oblong, with a bristle tip, narrowed to the base, up to 6 inches long, up to 2 inches wide, dark green, smooth and shiny on the upper surface, paler and hairy on the undersurface; petioles up to $1/2$ inch long, stout, hairy

Flowers: Monoecious; staminate and pistillate borne separately but on the same tree, appearing as the leaves begin to unfold, minute, without petals; staminate flowers in slender, yellow, drooping catkins; pistillate flowers few in a cluster

Fruit: Nut; acorns solitary or 2 together, stalked; nut nearly spherical, dark brown, less than one-half enclosed by the cup; cup reddish brown and slightly hairy; matures second season

Wood: Ring-porous; hard, heavy, coarse-grained, reddish brown

Uses: Commercial value; high-quality lumber, veneer, furniture, pulpwood, cabinets, flooring, paneling, interior finishing, railroad crossties, slack cooperage, mine timbers, fence posts, novelties, boxes, crates, blocking, pallets, and firewood

Habitat: A classic generalist; prefers well-drained bottomland forests; also thrives in upland forests that range in drainage and fertility; common to fencerows along agricultural fields

Range: Native to Illinois; New Jersey across to Wisconsin, Iowa, and Nebraska; south to Kansas; east to Arkansas and South Carolina

Distinguishing features: Only shingle oak and willow oak, among all Illinois oaks, have leaves without teeth or lobes. Shingle oak generally has broader leaves than does the willow oak.

Shingle Oak

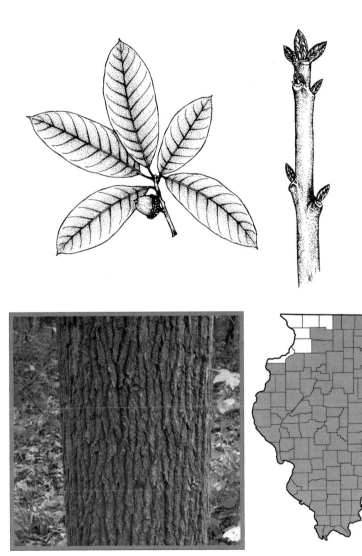

OVERCUP OAK
Quercus lyrata Walt.

Growth form: Medium-sized to large tree, up to 80 feet tall; trunk diameter up to 3 feet; crown rounded to oblong, with several branches, the lowermost often drooping; trunk straight, columnar

Bark: Gray or grayish brown, divided into flat, sometimes squarish, plates

Twigs: Slender, smooth, buff-colored; pith star-shaped in cross section; leaf scars alternate but clustered near the tip of the twig, half-round, slightly elevated, with several bundle traces

Buds: Nearly round, smooth, pale brown, up to $1/8$ inch long

Leaves: Alternate, simple; blades divided into 5 to 7 rounded lobes, the sinuses shallow to deep, up to 10 inches long, up to $4^1/2$ inches broad, dark green and smooth on the upper surface, pale and softly hairy to nearly smooth on the undersurface; petioles up to 1 inch long, smooth or hairy

Flowers: Monoecious; staminate and pistillate borne separately but on the same plant, appearing when the leaves begin to unfold, minute, without petals; staminate flowers in slender, yellow, drooping catkins; pistillate flowers few in a group

Fruit: Nut; acorns solitary or 2 together, with or without a stalk; nut nearly spherical, up to 1 inch in diameter, pale brown, often nearly entirely enclosed by the cup; cup finely hairy, with some of the scales forming a ragged rim near the base; matures first season

Wood: Ring-porous; hard, heavy, strong, light to dark brown

Uses: Commercial value; high-quality lumber, veneer, furniture, pulpwood, cabinets, flooring, paneling, interior finishing, railroad crossties, tight cooperage, mine timbers, fence posts, novelties, boxes, crates, blocking, pallets, and firewood

Habitat: Somewhat poorly drained to poorly drained bottomland forests; moisture-loving species capable of withstanding prolonged periods of inundation due to periodic flooding

Range: Native to Illinois; southern Virginia across to eastern Texas, north up the Mississippi Valley to southern Missouri, southern Illinois and southern Indiana; also in Delaware, Maryland and New Jersey; southward to Florida

Distinguishing features: The best identifying characteristic of this tree is the acorn, in which the nut is nearly enclosed by the cup.

Overcup Oak

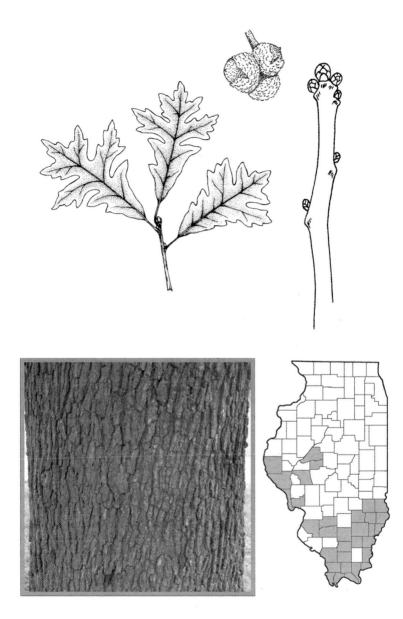

BUR OAK
Quercus macrocarpa Michx.

Other names: Mossycup oak

Growth form: Large tree, up to 120 feet tall; trunk diameter up to 5 feet; crown rounded, with stout branches; trunk straight, stout, sometimes slightly buttressed at the base

Bark: Dark brown or gray, shallow to deeply furrowed

Twigs: Stout, dark brown, often with corky ridges; pith star-shaped in cross section; leaf scars alternate but clustered near the tip, half-round, slightly elevated, with several bundle traces

Buds: Rounded or slightly pointed at the tip, yellowish brown to reddish brown, finely hairy

Leaves: Alternate, simple; blades broader at the upper end, coarsely round-toothed, usually with a pair of deep sinuses just below the middle, often with as many as 5 to 7 lobes, the lobes not bristle-tipped; dark green and smooth or slightly hairy on the upper surface, paler and softly hairy on the undersurface; up to 14 inches long and 7 inches wide; petioles up to 1 inch long, stout, smooth or finely hairy

Flowers: Monoecious; staminate and pistillate borne separately but on the same tree, appearing as the leaves begin to unfold, minute, without petals; staminate flowers in slender, drooping catkins; pistillate flowers few in a group, with red stigmas

Fruit: Nut; acorn usually solitary, with or without a stalk; nut ovoid to ellipsoid, dark brown, up to $1^3/4$ inches long; cup covering one-half to nearly all the nut, hairy, the uppermost scales long-fringed; matures first season

Wood: Ring-porous; heavy, hard, durable, close-grained, light to dark brown

Uses: A valuable timber species; high-quality lumber, face veneer, furniture, pulpwood, cabinets, flooring, paneling, interior finishing, railroad crossties, tight cooperage, general construction, mine timbers, fence posts, novelties, boxes, crates, blocking, pallets, and firewood

Habitat: A classic generalist; prefers rich, well-drained bottomland forests; thrives in upland forests that range in drainage and fertility

Range: Native to Illinois; Vermont across to North Dakota; south to Texas; east to Arkansas, Tennessee, and Maryland

Distinguishing features: The leaves of bur oak are distinctive because they are very broad in the upper half, with a pair of deep sinuses a little below the middle. The large, fringed acorn cups also are distinctive.

Bur Oak

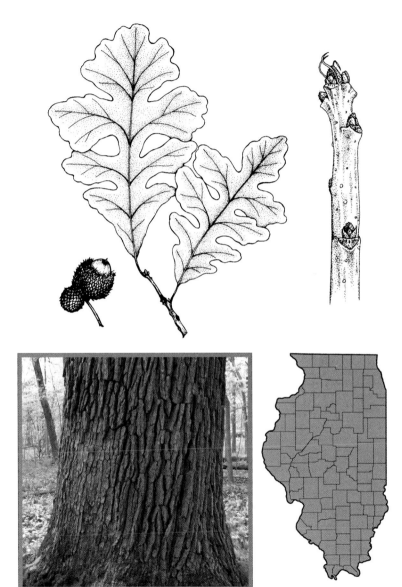

BLACKJACK OAK
Quercus marilandica Muenchh.

Growth form: Small to medium-sized tree, attaining a height of 60 feet, usually much
shorter and often very gnarled; trunk diameter up to $1^1/2$ feet; crown exceedingly
round-topped, with numerous lower branches hanging downward

Bark: Dark brown, shallowly ridged

Twigs: Moderately stout, brown, more or less hairy; pith star-shaped in cross section;
leaf scars alternate but clustered near the top, half-round, slightly elevated, with
several bundle traces

Buds: Angular, from $1/4$ to $1/2$ inch long, somewhat hairy

Leaves: Alternate, simple; blades about 4 to 8 inches long, leathery, very much broader
near the apex than the base, mostly rounded or even somewhat heart-shaped at
the base, more or less 3-lobed and bristle-tipped nearer the apex, the upper surface
hairy at first, becoming shiny dark green at maturity, the undersurface permanently
hairy; petioles less than 1 inch long

Flowers: Monoecious; staminate and pistillate on the same tree, appearing as the leaves
unfold, inconspicuous; staminate flowers crowded in a catkin; pistillate flowers solitary or 2 or 3 together

Fruit: Nut; acorn on very short stalks or the stalks sometimes lacking; acorns nearly
round, usually at most only $1/2$ inch in diameter; cup enclosing one-half the acorn,
with rather loosely arranged scales; matures second season

Wood: Ring-porous; hard, strong, heavy, reddish brown

Uses: Limited commercial value; lumber, pulpwood, railroad crossties, slack cooperage, general construction, mine timbers, fence posts, novelties, boxes, crates, blocking, pallets, and firewood

Habitat: Excessively drained to well-drained upland forests; characteristic of dry, gravelly, sandy soils with low fertility

Range: Native to Illinois; New York across to Pennsylvania, Ohio, Indiana, Illinois, and
southern Iowa to southeastern Nebraska; south into eastern Kansas, eastern
Oklahoma, and eastern Texas; then east to northern Florida

Distinguishing features: The three-lobed leaf, much broader at the apex, is the most
distinctive characteristic of this oak.

Blackjack Oak

SWAMP CHESTNUT OAK
Quercus michauxii Nutt.

Other names: Basket oak, cow oak

Growth form: Large tree, up to nearly 100 feet tall; trunk diameter up to 6 feet; crown rounded

Bark: Gray or silvery white, scaly to narrowly ridged

Twigs: Stout, reddish brown to gray, smooth or nearly so; leaf scars alternate but crowded near the tip, half-round, slightly elevated, with several bundle traces; pith star-shaped in cross section

Buds: Pointed, finely hairy, reddish brown, up to $1/4$ inch long

Leaves: Alternate, simple; blades obovate, pointed at the tip, rounded or tapering to the base, up to 10 inches long and 6 inches broad, coarsely scalloped along the edges; thick, green, and sparsely hairy on the upper surface; whitish and densely hairy on the undersurface; petioles up to $1^{1}/2$ inches long, hairy

Flowers: Monoecious; borne separately but on the same tree, minute, without petals; staminate flowers on long, slender catkins; pistillate flowers few in a cluster

Fruit: Nut; acorns solitary or paired, with or without short stalks; nut ovoid to ellipsoid, brown, up to $1^{1}/2$ inches long, enclosed about one-third its length by the cup; cup thick, hairy, short-fringed along the rim; matures first season

Wood: Ring-porous; hard, heavy, strong, close-grained, light to dark brown

Uses: A valuable timber species; high-quality lumber, face veneer, furniture, pulpwood, cabinets, flooring, interior finishing, railroad crossties, tight cooperage, mine timbers, crates, blocking, pallets, and firewood

Habitat: Moderately well-drained to somewhat poorly drained bottomland forests; attains its best development on deep, fertile, well-drained alluvial soils; contrary to its name, does not grow well in swampy environments

Range: Native to Illinois; New Jersey across to southern Missouri, south to Texas, east to Florida

Distinguishing features: Swamp chestnut oak is distinguished from other coarsely toothed oaks by the densely hairy, whitish underleaf surfaces and short-stalked acorns.

Swamp Chestnut Oak

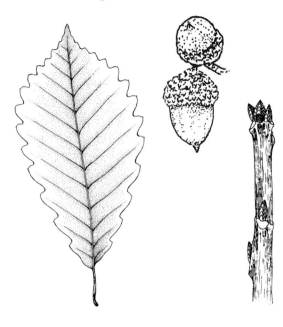

CHINKAPIN OAK
Quercus muehlenbergii Engelm.

Other names: Chinquapin oak, Yellow chestnut oak

Growth form: Large tree up to 100 feet tall; trunk diameter up to 4 feet; crown oblong
or rounded, with many branches; trunk straight, columnar, buttressed at the base

Bark: Light gray, with scaly ridges

Twigs: Slender, yellow–brown or reddish brown; pith star-shaped in cross section;
leaf scars alternate but clustered near the tip, half-round, with several bundle traces

Buds: Pointed, smooth, chestnut brown, up to $^1/_4$ inch long

Leaves: Alternate, simple; blades narrowly to broadly lanceolate, pointed at the tip,
narrowed or rounded at the base, coarsely toothed along the edges, smooth and
yellow–green on the upper surface, paler and usually finely hairy on the undersurface, up to 8 inches long and 5 inches broad; petioles up to $1^1/_2$ inches long,
slender, usually smooth

Flowers: Monoecious; staminate and pistillate borne separately, but on the same tree,
minute, without petals; staminate flowers crowded into long, slender catkins; pistillate flowers few in a group, with red stigmas

Fruit: Nut; acorns borne singly or paired, usually on a short stalk; nut ovoid,
chestnut-colored, up to $^3/_4$ inch long; cup covering about one-half the nut, the
scales of the cup hairy and usually with a short fringe; matures first season

Wood: Ring-porous; heavy, strong, durable, light to dark brown

Uses: A valuable timber species; high-quality lumber, face veneer, furniture, pulpwood,
cabinets, flooring, paneling, interior finishing, railroad crossties, tight cooperage,
general construction, mine timbers, fence posts, novelties, boxes, crates, blocking,
pallets, and firewood

Habitat: Well-drained to moderately well-drained upland forests; prefers alkaline, deep,
moist, upland sites including coves, low slopes and ravines; occasionally found on
terraced bottomland forest sites with excellent drainage

Range: Native to Illinois; Vermont across to southern Minnesota, south to eastern
Nebraska and eastern Texas, east to northern Florida

Distinguishing features: Chinkapin oak is distinguished from the other coarsely
toothed oaks by its usually sharper-pointed teeth and by the small size and shape
of its acorns.

Chinkapin Oak

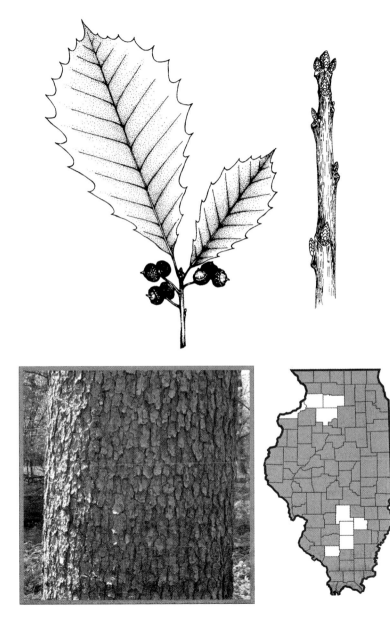

CHERRYBARK OAK
Quercus pagoda Raf.

Growth form: Large tree, up to 100 feet tall; trunk diameter up to 4 feet; crown broadly rounded; trunk straight, columnar

Bark: Dark gray, broken by narrow ridges into small scales; young tree bark resembles black cherry

Twigs: Rather stout, reddish brown or gray, usually hairy when young, becoming smooth; pith star-shaped in cross section; leaf scars alternate but clustered near tip of the twigs, half-round, slightly elevated, with several bundle traces

Buds: Ovoid, pointed, angular, hairy, chestnut brown, up to $1/4$ inch long

Leaves: Alternate, simple; blades divided into 5 to 11 pointed lobes, the sinuses cut about halfway to the midvein, up to 10 inches long, up to 7 inches wide; dark green, smooth and shiny on the upper surface; pale and hairy on the undersurface; petioles up to 2 inches long, stout, hairy

Flowers: Monoecious; staminate and pistillate borne separately but on the same plant, appearing when the leaves begin to unfold, minute, without petals; staminate flowers in slender, drooping catkins; pistillate flowers few together

Fruit: Nut; acorns solitary or 2 together, with or without a stalk; nut ellipsoid, about $1/2$ inch long, brown, enclosed for less than one-third its length by the cup; cup finely hairy; matures second season

Wood: Ring-porous; strong, hard, coarse-grained, reddish brown

Uses: A prized timber species; high-quality lumber, face veneer, furniture, pulpwood, cabinets, flooring, paneling, interior finishing, railroad crossties, slack cooperage, general construction, mine timbers, fence posts, novelties, boxes, crates, blocking, pallets, and firewood

Habitat: Moderately well-drained to somewhat poorly drained bottomland forests; by preference a bottomland species, however, occupies marginal to rich upland forest sites

Range: Native to Illinois; Southeastern Virginia to southeastern Missouri, south to Texas, east to Florida

Distinguishing features: The pagoda-shaped leaf base and characteristic bark are distinctive.

Cherrybark Oak

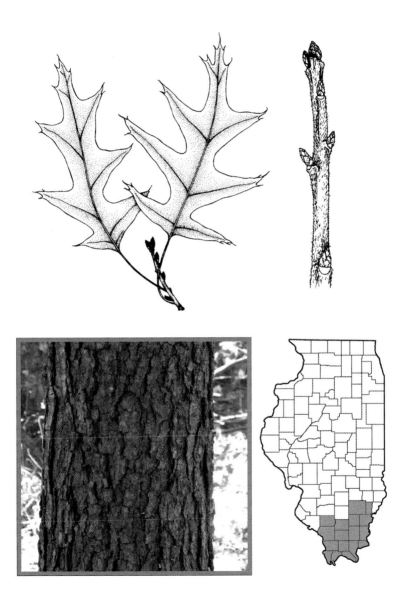

PIN OAK
Quercus palustris Muenchh.

Growth form: Large tree, up to 100 feet tall; trunk diameter up to 3 feet; crown narrowly rounded or oblong but with the lower branches drooping; trunk straight, with pinlike stubs developing rather low on the trunk

Bark: Light brown or dark brown, scarcely furrowed

Twigs: Slender, smooth, reddish brown to dark gray; pith star-shaped in cross section; leaf scars alternate but crowded near the tip, half-round, usually slightly elevated, with several bundle traces

Buds: Pointed, reddish brown or dark gray, smooth, up to $1/8$ inch long

Leaves: Alternate, simple; blades divided more than half way to the middle into 5 to 7 bristle-tipped lobes; dark green, shiny and more or less smooth on the upper surface, paler and with tufts of hairs along the veins on the undersurface; up to 7 inches long and 4 inches broad; petioles up to 2 inches long, slender, usually smooth

Flowers: Monoecious; staminate and pistillate borne separately but on the same tree, appearing when the leaves begin to unfold, minute, without petals; staminate flowers in slender, drooping catkins; pistillate flowers borne single or in groups of 2 or 3

Fruit: Nut; acorns 1 to 4 together, with or without stalks; nut hemispherical, up to $1/2$ inch across, pale brown, frequently with darker lines, enclosed less than one-fourth by the cup; cup thin, saucer-shaped, reddish brown, finely hairy; matures second season

Wood: Ring-porous; hard, heavy, coarse-grained, reddish brown

Uses: A valuable timber species; high-quality lumber, veneer, furniture, pulpwood, cabinets, flooring, paneling, interior finishing, railroad crossties, slack cooperage, general construction, mine timbers, fence posts, novelties, boxes, crates, blocking, pallets, and firewood; important food source for waterfowl

Habitat: Moderately well-drained to poorly drained bottomland forests; by preference a bottomland species, however occupies upland forest sites; also associated with flatwoods

Range: Native to Illinois; Massachusetts across to southeastern Iowa, south to northeastern Oklahoma, east to northern Virginia

Distinguishing features: Pin oak is recognized by its drooping lower branches and small acorns.

Pin Oak

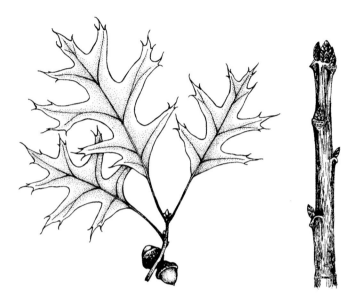

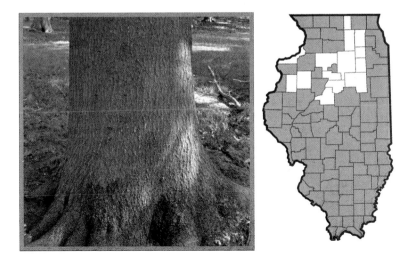

WILLOW OAK
Quercus phellos L.

Growth form: Medium-sized to large tree, up to 90 feet tall; trunk diameter up to 3 feet; crown narrowly round-topped

Bark: reddish brown, smooth at first, becoming irregularly and shallowly furrowed with age

Twigs: Slender, smooth, reddish brown; pith star-shaped in cross section; leaf scars alternate but crowded near the tip of the twigs, half-round, slightly elevated, with several bundle traces

Buds: Ovoid, pointed, smooth, up to $1/8$ inch long

Leaves: Alternate, simple; blades without lobes or teeth, narrowly lanceolate to narrowly oblong, with a bristle tip, narrowed to the base, up to 5 inches long, up to 1 inch broad, light green and smooth on the upper surface, usually smooth and paler on the undersurface; petioles up to $1/2$ inch long, smooth or slightly hairy

Flowers: Monoecious; staminate and pistillate borne separately but on the same tree, appearing as the leaves begin to unfold, minute, without petals; staminate flowers in slender, drooping catkins; pistillate flowers few in a cluster

Fruit: Nut; acorns solitary or paired, with or without a short stalk; nut more or less spherical, pale yellow–brown, enclosed less than $1/4$ its length by the cup; cup reddish brown, finely hairy; matures in second growing season

Wood: Ring-porous; heavy, strong, coarse-grained, reddish brown

Uses: Limited commercial value in Illinois; high-quality lumber, veneer, furniture, pulpwood, cabinets, flooring, paneling, interior finishing, railroad crossties, slack cooperage, general construction, mine timbers, fence posts, novelties, boxes, crates, blocking, pallets, and firewood

Habitat: Moderately well-drained to poorly drained bottomland forests; attains its best development on deep, fertile, well-drained alluvial soils

Range: Native to Illinois; New York across to southern Illinois and eastern Oklahoma, south to Texas, east to Florida

Distinguishing features: Willow oak and shingle oak are the only oaks in Illinois with unlobed, untoothed leaves. The leaves of the willow oak are usually much narrower than those of the shingle oak.

Willow Oak

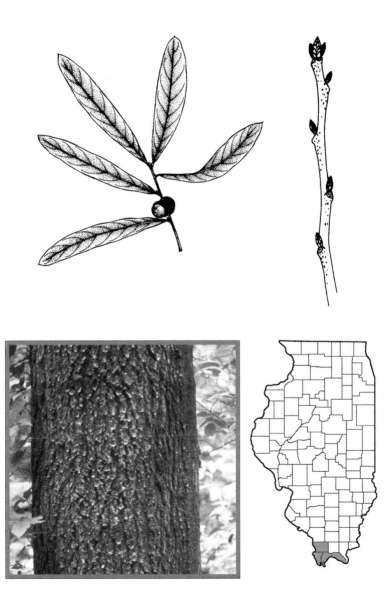

CHESTNUT OAK
Quercus prinus L.

Other names: Rock chestnut oak

Growth form: Medium-sized tree, up to 60 feet tall; trunk diameter up to $2^1/2$ feet; crown broad but irregular

Bark: Dark brown, with conspicuous furrows between the rounded ridges

Twigs: Rather stout, reddish brown, smooth or nearly so; leaf scars alternate but clustered near the tip of the twig, half-round, with several bundle traces; pith star-shaped in cross section

Buds: Pointed, brown, somewhat hairy, up to $1/2$ inch long

Leaves: Alternate, simple; blades obovate to broadly lanceolate, pointed at tip, narrowed to base, thick and leathery, coarsely round-toothed along edges, smooth, shiny and yellow–green on upper surface, finely hairy on undersurface, up to 9 inches long and 4 inches broad; petiole up to 1 inch long, smooth or slightly hairy

Flowers: Monoecious; staminate and pistillate borne separately but on the same tree, minute, without petals; staminate flowers crowded into long, slender catkins; pistillate flowers few in a group

Fruit: Nut; acorns borne singly or paired, usually on a short stalk; nut ovoid to ellipsoid, chestnut-colored, up to $1^1/2$ inches long; cup covering about one-half the nut or less, the scales of the cup reddish brown and warty; matures first season

Wood: Ring-porous; hard, heavy, strong, light to dark brown

Uses: Limited commercial value in Illinois; lumber, veneer, furniture, pulpwood, cabinets, flooring, interior finishing, railroad crossties, cooperage, mine timbers, blocking, pallets, and firewood

Habitat: Excessively drained to well-drained upland forests; commonly found on dry, gravelly ridge tops and upland slopes

Range: Native to Illinois; Maine across to southern Illinois, south to Mississippi and Georgia

Distinguishing features: Acorns of chestnut oak are about twice the size as those of the chinkapin oak. The teeth of the leaves of the chestnut oak tend to be more rounded than the pointed teeth of the chinkapin oak.

Chestnut Oak

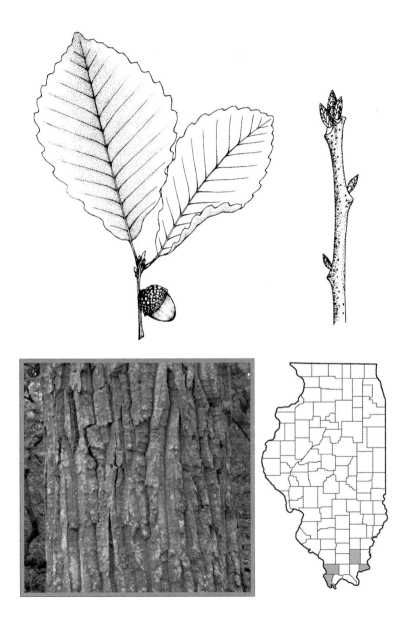

NORTHERN RED OAK
Quercus rubra L.

Growth form: Large tree, up to 120 feet tall; trunk diameter up to 4 feet; crown broadly rounded, with large spreading branches; trunk straight, columnar, often buttressed at the base

Bark: Grayish brown, reddish brown, blackish, or gray, with dark stripes; becoming deeply furrowed on old trees

Twigs: Slender, smooth, reddish brown; pith star-shaped in cross section; leaf scars alternate but clustered near the tip of the twig, half-round, slightly elevated, with several bundle traces

Buds: Pointed, smooth, reddish brown, shiny, up to $1/4$ inch long

Leaves: Alternate, simple; blades rather shallowly 7- to 11-lobed, the lobes bristle-tipped, dark green, and smooth or somewhat hairy on the upper surface, paler and smooth or often with hairs along the veins on the lower surface, up to 10 inches long, up to 6 inches broad; petioles up to 2 inches long, stout, usually smooth and reddish

Flowers: Monoecious; staminate and pistillate borne separately but on the same tree, appearing as the leaves begin to unfold, minute, without petals; staminate flowers in slender, drooping catkins; pistillate flowers borne singly or in groups of 2 or 3

Fruit: Nut; acorns solitary or 2 together, with or without stalks; nut ovoid, up to $1^1/2$ inches long, pale brown, covered less than one-fourth by the cup; cup reddish brown, with tight scales; matures second season

Wood: Ring-porous; hard, heavy, reddish brown

Uses: A prized timber species; high-quality lumber, face veneer, furniture, pulpwood, cabinets, flooring, paneling, interior finishing, railroad crossties, slack cooperage, general construction, mine timbers, fence posts, novelties, boxes, crates, blocking, pallets, and firewood

Habitat: Well-drained to moderately well-drained upland forests; prefers rich, deep, moist upland sites including coves, low slopes, and ravines

Range: Native to Illinois; New Brunswick, across southern Quebec and Ontario, to north-central Minnesota, south to eastern Kansas; east across Missouri, Illinois, and Kentucky, and in the mountains of eastern Tennessee and northeastern Georgia

Distinguishing features: The acorn with its very shallow, saucer-shaped cap is the best identifying characteristic for northern red oak. The leaves are generally more shallowly lobed than those of black oak, southern red oak, and scarlet oak.

Northern Red Oak

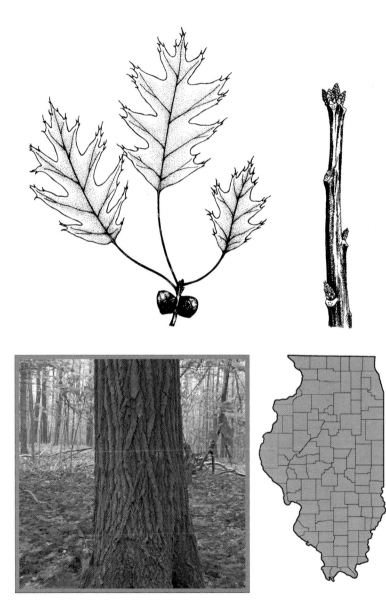

SHUMARD OAK
Quercus shumardii Buckl.

Growth form: Large tree, up to 120 feet tall; trunk up to 5 feet in diameter; crown broad and open, with wide-spreading branches

Bark: Dark brownish black, becoming deeply furrowed (similar to northern red oak)

Twigs: Generally stouter than those of northern red oak, smooth; pith star-shaped in cross section; leaf scars alternate, but clustered near the tip of the twig, half-round, slightly elevated, with several bundle traces

Buds: Smooth, red–brown, about $1/3$ inch long

Leaves: Alternate, simple; blades up to 8 inches long, straight across or somewhat wedge-shaped at the base, with 2 to 4 pairs of lobes divided more than two-thirds of the way to the midrib, each lobe toothed and bristle-pointed at the tips, the sinuses broadly rounded, dark green and shiny above, with white tufts of hair in the vein axils beneath; petioles slender, smooth, up to $2^{1}/2$ inches long

Flowers: Monoecious; staminate and pistillate on the same tree, appearing as the leaves unfold, inconspicuous; staminate flowers crowded in a catkin; pistillate flowers solitary or 2 to 3 together

Fruit: Nut; acorn, on stalks less than $1/4$ inch long, usually produced singly; acorns broadly egg-shaped, short-pointed at the base and flat at the top, up to $1^{1}/4$ inches long and about $3/4$ as broad, light brown; cup shallow, about one-fourth to one-third covering the acorn, with closely appressed, densely short-woolly scales; matures second season

Wood: Ring-porous, heavy, strong, durable

Uses: A prized timber species; high-quality lumber, face veneer, furniture, pulpwood, cabinets, flooring, paneling, interior finishing, railroad crossties, slack cooperage, general construction, mine timbers, fence posts, novelties, boxes, crates, blocking, pallets, and firewood

Habitat: Moderately well-drained to somewhat poorly drained bottomland forests; by preference a bottomland species but occupies marginal to rich upland forest sites

Range: Native to Illinois; most abundant in the Mississippi basin but known from Florida and Texas; north to Maryland, Pennsylvania, east-central Kentucky, Indiana, central Illinois, the eastern half of Iowa, and southeastern Kansas.

Distinguishing features: Shumard oak has deeply lobed, shiny leaves with broadly rounded sinuses.

Shumard Oak

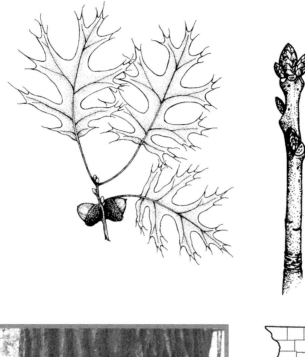

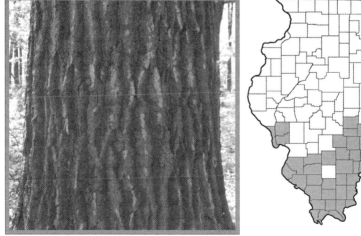

POST OAK
Quercus stellata Wangenh.

Growth form: Medium-sized to large tree, up to 90 feet tall; trunk diameter up to 3 feet; crown rounded or obovoid, with rather stout branches; trunk gnarled or straight, usually not buttressed

Bark: Gray or light brown, divided into flat, sometimes squarish, plates

Twigs: Stout, brownish, covered when young by a tawny-colored fuzziness; pith star-shaped in cross section; leaf scars alternate but densely clustered toward the tip, half-round, usually slightly elevated, with several bundle traces

Buds: Spherical but often short-pointed, reddish brown, up to $1/8$ inch long

Leaves: Alternate, simple; blades thick, 5-lobed, the upper 3 lobes squarish, separated from the lowest pair of lobes by a deep sinus, up to 6 inches long, up to $4^1/2$ inches wide, dark green and hairy on the upper surface, paler and hairy on the undersurface; petioles up to 1 inch long, stout, hairy

Flowers: Monoecious; staminate and pistillate borne separately but on the same tree, appearing when the leaves begin to unfold, minute, without petals; staminate flowers in slender, yellow, drooping catkins; pistillate flowers few in a cluster

Fruit: Nut; acorns solitary or paired, with or without a short stalk; nut oval to oblong, up to 1 inch long, pale brown, less than one-half enclosed by the cup; cup reddish brown, hairy; matures first year

Wood: Ring-porous; hard, light to dark brown

Uses: A valuable timber species; high-quality lumber, veneer, furniture, pulpwood, cabinets, flooring, paneling, interior finishing, railroad crossties, tight cooperage, general construction, mine timbers, fence posts, novelties, boxes, crates, blocking, pallets, and firewood

Habitat: Excessively drained to well-drained upland forests; commonly found on dry, gravelly ridge tops and upland slopes; also associated with flatwoods

Range: Native to Illinois; Massachusetts across to Kansas, south to Texas, east to Florida

Distinguishing features: The three squarish lobes at the upper end of the thick leaves distinguish post oak.

Post Oak

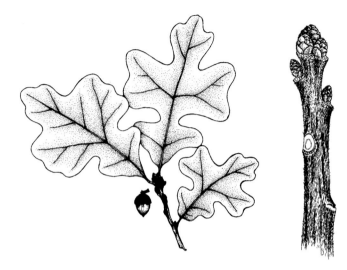

NUTTALL OAK
Quercus texana Buckl.

Growth form: Medium-sized to large tree, up to 100 feet tall; trunk diameter up to 3 feet; well-developed, open crown of spreading branches; rapid growth rate

Bark: Gray to gray–brown, smooth; on older trees broken into broad flat ridges divided by narrow lighter-colored fissures similar to that of pin oak; on thrifty specimens, bark on the upper bole frequently fissured vertically, exposing light brown inner bark

Twigs: Moderately slender, gray–brown to reddish brown, glabrous or sparsely pubescent, ending in a cluster of blunt, brown buds

Buds: Terminal nearly $1/4$ inch long, ovoid, slightly angled; with numerous gray–brown, glabrous or slightly downy scales

Leaves: Alternate, simple; leaves 4 to 8 inches long, 2 to 5 inches wide; shape obovate; margin usually 5 to 7 (rarely 9) lobes rather broad, separated by deep, wide sinuses ending in bristle-tipped teeth; terminal lobe usually elongated, upper lobes curve slightly toward the leaf tip; middle lobes tend to be at right angles to midrib; apex acute to acuminate; base truncate to broadly cuneate; leaf surface dull dark green above, paler with tufts of hair in vein angles below; autumn color brownish red

Flowers: Monoecious; male and female flowers appear in March and April at leaf flushing; male flowers borne in clustered, yellowish green catkins; inconspicuous female flowers borne in axils of new leaves and found only by close examination

Fruit: Nut; acorn solitary or clustered; nut $3/4$ to $1 1/4$ inches long, oblong–ovoid, reddish brown, often striated, enclosed in a stalked, nipple-shaped, thick cup; cup scales somewhat scaly; matures second season

Wood: Ring-porous; hard, heavy, strong, reddish brown

Uses: Limited commercial value in Illinois; high-quality lumber, face veneer, furniture, pulpwood, cabinets, flooring, paneling, interior finishing, railroad crossties, slack cooperage, general construction, mine timbers, fence posts, novelties, boxes, crates, blocking, pallets, and firewood

Habitat: Moderately well-drained to poorly drained bottomland forests; attains its best development on deep, fertile, well-drained alluvial soils

Range: Restricted to southernmost counties in Illinois; species of very limited range, native to the lower Mississippi Valley and Gulf Coastal Plain from Alabama to Texas

Distinguishing features: Nuttall oak resembles pin oak except it has larger, longer acorns and fewer retained, dead side branches. Terminal lobe is usually elongated, and upper lobes curve slightly toward the leaf tip; middle lobes tend to be at right angles to the midrib.

Nuttall Oak

BLACK OAK
Quercus velutina Lam.

Growth form: Large tree, up to 100 feet tall; trunk diameter up to $3^1/2$ feet; crown broadly rounded or oblong, with spreading branches; trunk straight, columnar, scarcely buttressed at the base

Bark: Black, with a yellow or orange inner bark, deeply furrowed

Twigs: Slender or rather stout, reddish brown to dark brown; pith star-shaped in cross section; leaf scars alternate but clustered near the tip, half-round, slightly elevated, with several bundle traces

Buds: Pointed, angular, gray or reddish brown, hairy, up to $1/2$ inch long

Leaves: Alternate, simple; blades deeply to shallowly 7- to 9-lobed, the lobes bristle-tipped, dark green, shiny and usually smooth on the upper surface; smooth, finely hairy, or hairy only along the veins on the undersurface; up to 10 inches long and 8 inches wide; petioles up to 5 inches long, stout, smooth or finely hairy

Flowers: Monoecious; staminate and pistillate borne separately but on the same tree, appearing when the leaves begin to unfold, minute, without petals; staminate flowers in slender, drooping clusters; pistillate flowers borne singly or in groups of 2 to 4

Fruit: Nut; acorns solitary or 2 together, with or without a short stalk; nut ovoid or ellipsoid, up to $3/4$ inch long, reddish brown, not more than one-half enclosed by the cup; cup with scales not appressed at the tip, thus appearing ragged; matures second season

Wood: Ring-porous; hard, heavy, coarse-grained, reddish brown

Uses: A valuable timber species; high-quality lumber, veneer, furniture, pulpwood, cabinets, flooring, paneling, interior finishing, railroad crossties, slack cooperage, general construction, mine timbers, fence posts, novelties, boxes, crates, blocking, pallets, and firewood

Habitat: Excessively drained to well-drained upland forests; best development occurs on rich, deep, moist upland sites; more commonly found on dry upland forest sites

Range: Maine across to south-central Minnesota, south to eastern Texas, east to northern Florida

Distinguishing features: Black oak is easily distinguished by its large, angular, gray, hairy buds and acorns with a ragged-edged cup.

Black Oak

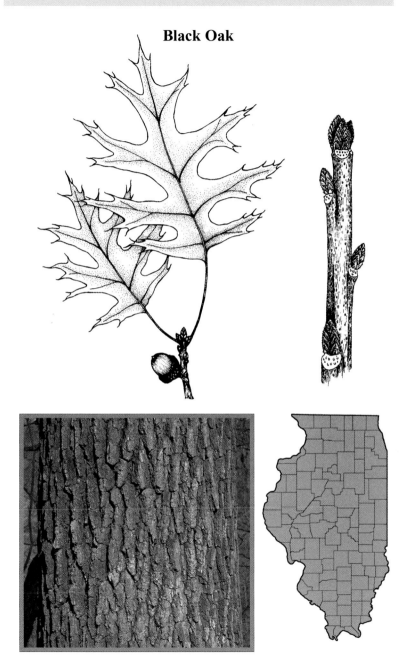

EUROPEAN BUCKTHORN
Rhamnus cathartica L.

Other names: Common buckthorn

Growth form: Small tree, up to 25 feet tall, often branching from near the base; trunk diameter up to 10 inches; crown spreading and irregular

Bark: Gray to brown, roughened when mature

Twigs: Gray to brown, usually smooth, some of them usually ending in a spine; leaf scars opposite to nearly so, narrow, with 3 bundle traces

Buds: Lanceolate, brown, smooth, up to $1/4$ inch long

Leaves: Broadly elliptic to ovate to nearly orbicular, rounded to pointed at the tip, usually rounded at the base, up to $2^1/2$ inches long and up to $1^1/2$ inches wide, finely toothed along the edges, smooth on both surfaces, the veins prominent; petioles slender, smooth, up to 1 inch long

Flowers: Polygamo-monoecious; borne in clusters from the axils of the leaves during May and June, some of them either only staminate or only pistillate, some with both stamens and pistils, each flower with 4 small petals

Fruit: Drupe; nearly round, fleshy, black, up to $1/4$ inch in diameter, bitter, containing 3 or 4 seeds

Wood: Diffuse-porous; heavy, hard, durable, yellowish, fine-grained

Uses: Ornamental hedge, tool handles, fruits as a powerful purging agent

Habitat: Thickets

Range: Introduced (Europe & Asia); naturalized and invasive throughout Illinois

Distinguishing features: The spine-tipped twigs, nearly opposite leaves, and small black fruits readily distinguish this species.

European Buckthorn

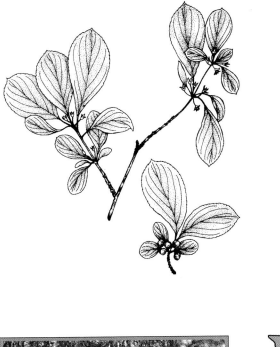

SHINING SUMAC
Rhus copallina L.

Other names: Winged sumac

Growth form: Small tree (shrub), up to 25 feet tall; trunk diameter up to 6 inches; crown widely spreading

Bark: Dark brown, roughened

Twigs: Rather stout, gray–brown to reddish brown, sometimes hairy, with conspicuous red lenticels; leaf scars alternate, U-shaped, elevated with 6 to 9 bundle traces

Buds: More or less rounded, rusty-hairy, about 1/8 inch long

Leaves: Alternate, pinnately compound, with as many as 21 leaflets; leaflets oblong to elliptic, up to 3 inches long and 1 inch broad, sharp-pointed at the apex, tapering or rounded at the sometimes asymmetrical base, smooth or with low teeth along the edges; dark green, smooth and shiny on the upper surface; paler and hairy on the undersurface; all leaflets attached to a winged rachis; autumn color deep red or wine

Flowers: Polygamo-dioecious; staminate and pistillate sometimes borne on separate plants, sometimes on the same plant, sometimes in the same flower; numerous in much-branched clusters, appearing from late May to mid-August, each flower greenish yellow, small

Fruit: Cluster of red berries, each berry round, finely hairy, up to 1/8 inch in diameter, containing a single orange seed

Wood: Ring-porous to semi-ring-pourous; lightweight, soft, greenish to reddish brown

Uses: Sometimes grown as an ornamental

Habitat: Dry hills, fields

Range: Native to Illinois; Maine across southern Michigan to eastern Nebraska, south to Texas, east to Florida

Distinguishing features: Shining sumac is readily distinguished by the winged rachis to which the leaflets are attached.

Shining Sumac

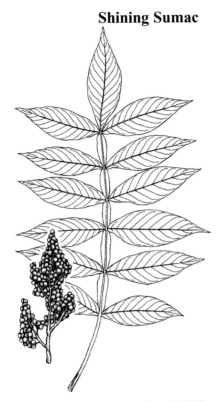

SMOOTH SUMAC
Rhus glabra L.

Growth form: Small tree (shrub), up to 20 feet tall; trunk diameter up to 8 inches; crown widely spreading

Bark: Light brown, smooth on young plants, becoming somewhat rough at maturity

Twigs: Stout, angular, smooth, reddish brown or greenish brown and covered by a whitish coat that can be wiped off, leaf scars alternate, nearly encircling the bud, elevated, with 6 to 9 bundle traces

Buds: Rounded, smooth, about $1/8$ inch long

Leaves: Alternate, pinnately compound, with up to 31 leaflets; leaflets lance-shaped, up to 4 inches long, less than 2 inches broad, sharp-pointed at the apex, tapering or rounded at the often asymmetrical base, toothed along the edges, green and smooth on the upper surface, nearly white and smooth on the undersurface; autumn color red

Flowers: Polygamo-dioecious; staminate and pistillate sometimes borne on separate plants, sometimes on the same plant, sometimes in the same flower; numerous in much-branched clusters, appearing from late May to mid-August, each flower greenish yellow, small

Fruit: Cluster of red berries, each berry round, smooth, up to $1/8$ inch in diameter, containing a single brown seed

Wood: Lightweight, soft, greenish to reddish brown

Uses: Sometimes grown as an ornamental

Habitat: Forests, fields, disturbed areas

Range: Native to Illinois; Nova Scotia across to Manitoba and North Dakota, south to Texas, east to Florida; also in Mexico

Distinguishing features: This species lacks the winged rachis of the shining sumac and lacks the velvety twigs of the staghorn sumac.

Smooth Sumac

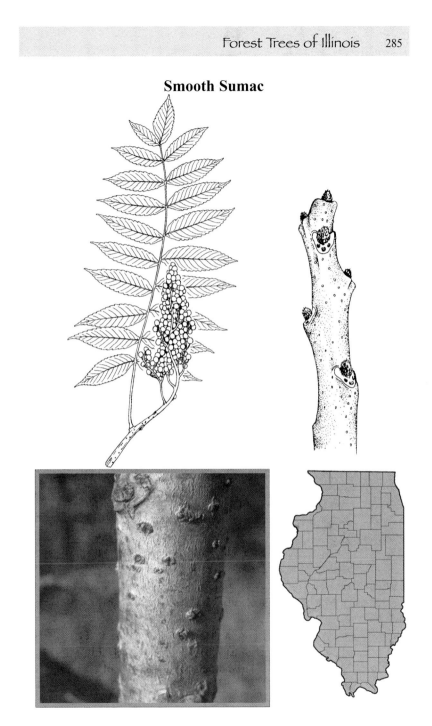

STAGHORN SUMAC
Rhus hirta (L.) Sudworth

Growth form: Small tree (shrub), up to 30 feet tall; trunk diameter up to 15 inches; crown broadly rounded or sometimes flat

Bark: Dark brown, smooth at first, becoming scaly in age

Twigs: Stout, dark brown, covered by velvety hairs; leaf scars nearly encircling the twigs, with 6 to 9 bundle traces

Buds: Rounded, hairy, about $1/8$ inch long

Leaves: Alternate, pinnately compound, with up to 31 sessile leaflets; leaflets lance-shaped, up to 5 inches long, less than 2 inches broad, pointed at the tip, tapering or rounded at the usually asymmetrical base, toothed along the edges, dark green and smooth on the upper surface, paler and smooth except for the hairy veins on the undersurface; autumn colors purple to red to orange

Flowers: Polygamo-dioecious; staminate and pistillate sometimes borne on separate plants, sometimes on the same plant, sometimes in the same flower; numerous in much-branched clusters, appearing from June to August, each flower greenish, greenish yellow, or reddish

Fruit: Dense cluster of red berries, each berry round, conspicuously hairy, up to $1/8$ inch in diameter, containing a single brown seed

Wood: Lightweight, soft, greenish to reddish brown

Uses: Sometimes grown as an ornamental

Habitat: Forests and thickets

Range: Native to Illinois; Nova Scotia across to Minnesota, south to Iowa and Kentucky, east to North Carolina

Distinguishing features: The densely velvety twigs are distinctive for this species.

Staghorn Sumac

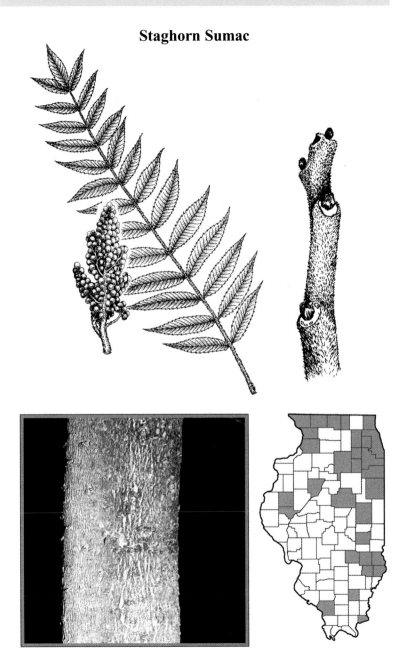

BLACK LOCUST
Robinia pseudoacacia L.

Growth form: Medium-sized tree, up to 80 feet tall; trunk diameter up to $2^1/2$ feet; crown narrowly oblong, with irregularly ascending or spreading branches

Bark: Gray or black, deeply furrowed, with numerous elevated, scaly ridges

Twigs: Slender but strong, angular, often zigzag, reddish brown, with a pair of short, sharp thorns where each leaf is attached; leaf scars alternate, 3-lobed, with 3 bundle traces per lobe

Buds: Sunken in the twigs, dark brown, without bud scales, up to $1/8$ inch long

Leaves: Alternate, pinnately compound, with 7 to 21 leaflets; leaflets oval, rounded at both ends but usually with a short point at the tip, without teeth, blue–green and smooth on the upper surface, paler and smooth on the undersurface except for the veins, up to 2 inches long and nearly one-half as wide; autumn color yellow

Flowers: Perfect; in long, drooping clusters; white with a yellow spot, very fragrant, up to 1 inch long, appearing in May and June

Fruit: Legume; up to 4 inches long and about $1/2$ inch wide, flat, smooth, reddish brown, with 4 to 8 seeds

Wood: Ring-porous; hard, heavy, strong, decay-resistant, greenish yellow to dark brown

Uses: Commercial value; lumber, pulpwood, posts, railroad crossties, general construction, mine timbers, fence posts, novelties, boxes, crates, blocking, pallets, and firewood; mine reclamation due to nitrogen fixation

Habitat: A classic generalist; prefers nutrient-rich, well-drained forests; occurs in a variety of disturbed habitats, including pastures, grazed woodlands, old fields, roadsides, and other rights-of-way; naturalized in many upland forests, prairies, and savannas

Range: Native to Illinois; Pennsylvania across to Oklahoma, east to Georgia; often planted in other regions of the eastern United States

Distinguishing features: The pinnately compound leaves with up to 21 oval, smooth-edged leaflets, together with the pairs of spines, serve to distinguish this species.

Black Locust

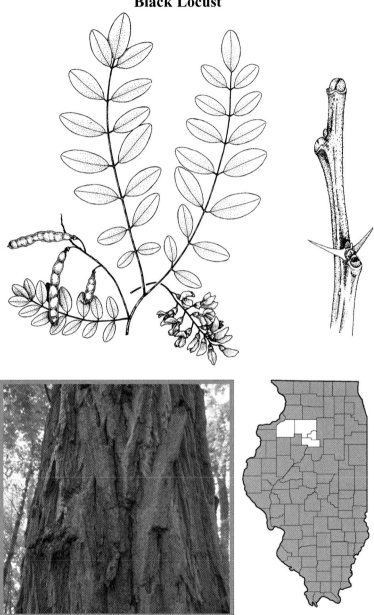

PEACHLEAF WILLOW
Salix amygdaloides Anderss.

Growth form: Medium-sized tree, up to 60 feet tall; trunk diameter up to $1^1/2$ feet; crown narrowly rounded

Bark: Grayish brown, shallowly furrowed, becoming somewhat scaly

Twigs: Slender, pale brown to grayish, smooth; leaf scars alternate, U-shaped, with 3 bundle traces

Buds: Small, oblong, brown, up to 1/6 inch long

Leaves: Alternate, simple; blades broadly lance-shaped, long-pointed at the tip, rounded or tapering to the base, up to 5 inches long, finely toothed along the edges, dark green and shiny on the upper surface, pale on the undersurface; petioles up to $1/2$ inch long

Flowers: Dioecious; staminate and pistillate flowers borne on separate trees, minute, crowded into elongated catkins, appearing as the leaves begin to unfold

Fruit: Capsule; several rather broad, flask-shaped, brown, up to 1/6 inch long, crowded in elongated clusters

Wood: Semi-ring to diffuse-porous; lightweight, soft, interlocked-grain, gray–brown color

Uses: Biomass, firewood; erosion control

Habitat: Along streams, around lakes and ponds

Range: Native to Illinois; Vermont across southern Ontario to British Columbia, south to New Mexico, east across southern Illinois to central New York

Distinguishing features: This willow has broader leaves than almost any other willow in Illinois. The pale lower surface of the leaves also distinguishes it from black willow.

Peachleaf Willow

COASTAL PLAIN WILLOW
Salix caroliniana Michx.

Other names: Ward willow, Carolina willow

Growth form: Medium-sized tree, up to 40 feet tall; trunk diameter up to 1 foot; crown widely spreading, often irregular

Bark: Dark brown to gray to black; scaly and ridged

Twigs: Slender, brown, usually finely hairy; leaf scars alternate, U-shaped, with 3 bundle traces

Buds: Small, oblong, reddish brown, smooth, up to $1/8$ inch long

Leaves: Alternate, simple; blades lanceolate, long-pointed at the tip, tapering to the base, up to 5 inches long and up to 1 inch broad, finely toothed along the edges, green and smooth on the upper surface, whitish and smooth on the undersurface; stipules conspicuous; petioles up to $1/2$ inch long, hairy

Flowers: Dioecious; staminate and pistillate flowers borne on separate trees, appearing as the leaves begin to unfold, crowded in elongated, yellowish, hairy catkins

Fruit: Capsule; several narrow, flask-shaped, brownish capsules up to $1/4$ inch long, crowded in elongated clusters

Wood: Semi-ring to diffuse-porous; lightweight, soft, not strong

Uses: Firewood; streambank stabilization projects

Habitat: Moist forests, along streams

Range: Native to Illinois; Maryland across southern Illinois to Kansas, south to Texas and Florida

Distinguishing features: The leaves of the coastal plain willow are shaped similarly to those of the black willow but differ by being whitened on the undersurface.

Coastal Plain Willow

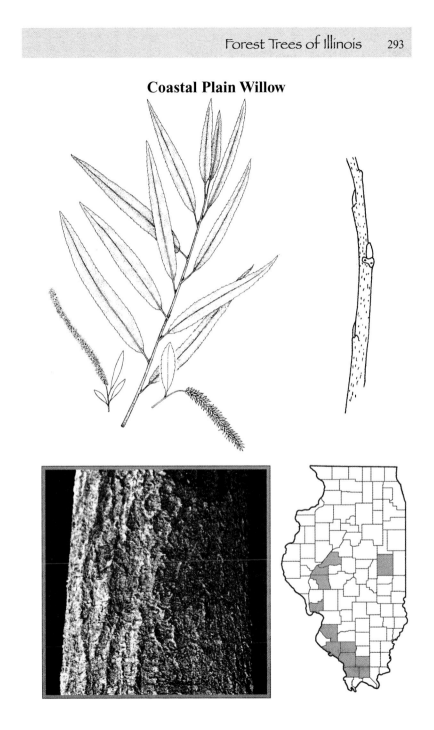

SANDBAR WILLOW
Salix exigua Nutt.

Growth form: Small tree, up to 25 feet tall; trunk diameter less than 12 inches; crown irregular

Bark: Gray, furrowed, broken into rough scales

Twigs: Slender, grayish green, smooth; leaf scars alternate, U-shaped, with 3 bundle traces

Buds: Small, oblong, pale brown, up to $1/6$ inch long

Leaves: Alternate, simple; blades very narrow, pointed at the tip, tapering to the base, to 4 inches long, less than $1/2$ inch broad, with widely spaced teeth along the edges, green and usually smooth on both surfaces when mature; petioles nearly absent

Flowers: Dioecious; staminate and pistillate flowers borne on separate trees, minute, crowded into elongated catkins, appearing when the leaves are partly grown

Fruit: Capsule; several flask-shaped, brownish, smooth or silky, up to $1/8$ inch long, crowded in elongated clusters

Wood: Semi-ring to diffuse-porous; lightweight, soft, weak

Uses: Firewood; streambank stabilization projects

Habitat: Along streams, often forming thickets

Range: Native to Illinois; Quebec across to Alaska, south to Oklahoma and Arkansas, east to Maryland

Distinguishing features: The best characteristics to identify this small tree are the narrow leaves with widely spaced teeth.

Sandbar Willow

BLACK WILLOW
Salix nigra Marsh.

Growth form: Medium-sized to large tree, up to 80 feet tall; trunk diameter up to 3 feet; crown usually round-topped, but sometimes irregular

Bark: Rough, furrowed, forming elongated, vertical, rather tight scales

Twigs: Slender, olive green, smooth; leaf scars alternate, U-shaped, with 3 bundle traces

Buds: Small, oblong, reddish brown, up to $1/8$ inch long

Leaves: Alternate, simple; blades narrowly lance-shaped, usually curved, long-pointed at the tip, rounded or tapering at the base, up to 6 inches long, finely toothed along the edges, green and shiny on the upper surface, smooth or hairy on the veins of the undersurface; petioles short, often surrounded at the base by a pair of green, leaf-like stipules

Flowers: Dioecious; staminate and pistillate flowers borne on separate trees, minute, crowded in elongated catkins, appearing as the leaves begin to unfold

Fruit: Capsule; several narrow, flask-shaped, reddish brown, up to $1/8$ inch long, crowded in elongated clusters

Wood: Semi-ring to diffuse-porous; lightweight, soft, interlocked-grain, red–brown to gray–brown

Uses: Pulpwood, boxes, crates, and firewood; streambank stabilization projects

Habitat: Prefers poorly drained bottomland forests, swamps, and low wet banks of streams

Range: Native to Illinois; New Brunswick across to Ontario, south to Texas, east to Florida

Distinguishing features: The narrow lance-shaped leaves, which are green on the undersurface and have many fine teeth along the edges, distinguish this species from other willows in Illinois.

Black Willow

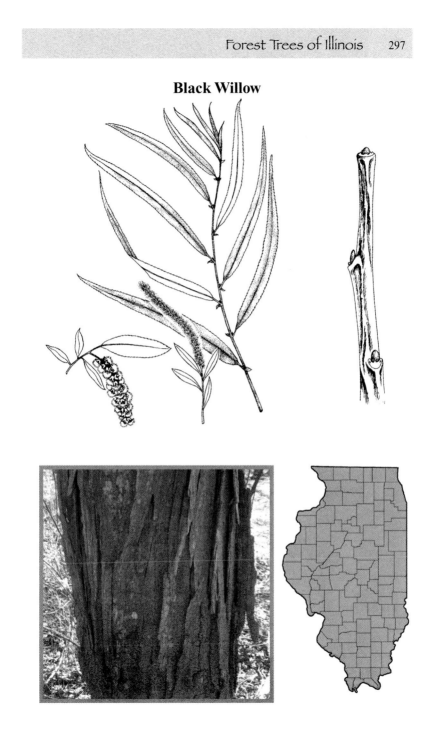

SASSAFRAS
Sassafras albidum (Nutt.) Nees

Growth form: Medium-sized tree, up to 70 feet tall; trunk diameter usually up to 2 feet; crown flat-topped, irregular, oblong

Bark: Greenish gray when young, becoming deeply furrowed and dark reddish brown when older

Twigs: Slender, green, smooth, aromatic; leaf scars alternate, small, half-round, usually with 3 bundle traces

Buds: Ovoid, scarcely pointed at the tip, greenish, up to $1/4$ inch long

Leaves: Alternate, simple; blades of 3 different shapes, some 3-lobed, some 2-lobed, some unlobed; tapering to the base, up to 6 inches long, without teeth along the edges, green and smooth on the upper surface, paler and either smooth or hairy on the undersurface; autumn colors orange, red, and yellow

Flowers: Dioecious; staminate and pistillate flowers borne on separate trees, in few-flowered clusters as the leaves begin to unfold, each flower about $1/3$ inch long, greenish yellow

Fruit: Drupe; dark blue berries about $1/3$ inch long in deep red cups and on stalks up to 2 inches long

Wood: Semi-ring-porous; soft, brittle, coarse-grained, orange–brown

Uses: Limited commercial value in Illinois; oils, roots, slack cooperage, mine timbers, lumber, fence posts, novelties, boxes, crates, blocking, pallets, and firewood

Habitat: Excessively drained to well-drained upland forests; characteristic of drier, poorer soils

Range: Native to Illinois; Maine across to Michigan, south to Texas, east to Florida

Distinguishing features: Sassafras is distinguished by its distinctively shaped, aromatic leaves and green twigs.

Sassafras

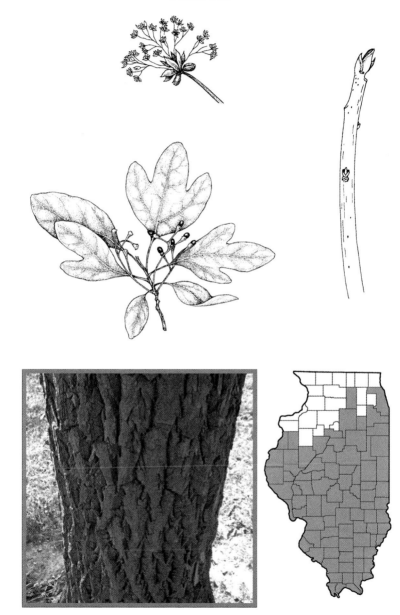

BALDCYPRESS
Taxodium distichum (L.) L.C. Rich.

Growth form: Large tree, up to 100 feet tall; trunk diameter up to 8 feet; crown open and spreading to pyramidal; base of trunk often swollen; "knees" usually produced if tree is growing in water

Bark: Pale reddish brown, broken into numerous thin scales, becoming fibrous

Twigs: Slender, reddish brown; leaf scars absent

Buds: Spherical, up to $1/8$ inch in diameter, pale brown

Leaves: Borne singly, pointed at the tip, up to $3/4$ inch long, yellow–green, falling away during autumn

Flowers: Monoecious; staminate borne in branched clusters up to 5 inches long, purplish; pistillate few to several near the ends of the twigs, spherical

Fruit: Cone; nearly spherical, up to 1 inch in diameter, green to brown, wrinkled in appearance

Wood: Moderately hard, extremely durable, lightweight, yellow–white to reddish color

Uses: A valuable timber species; high-quality lumber, veneer, doors, interior trim, boats, river pilings, bridges, fencing, decking material, fence posts, novelties, boxes, crates, blocking, pallets, and firewood

Habitat: Prefers poorly drained bottomland forests, swamps, and low wet banks of streams

Range: Native to Illinois; New Jersey across to southern Illinois and southern Missouri to eastern Texas, east to Florida

Distinguishing features: Baldcypress is distinguished by the feathery appearance of its leaves and by its spherical, wrinkled cones.

Baldcypress

NORTHERN WHITE-CEDAR
Thuja occidentalis L.

Other names: Eastern white-cedar, swamp-cedar, arborvitae

Growth form: Medium-sized tree, 40 to 60 feet tall; trunk diameter up to 2 feet; crown narrow to broadly pyramidal; long-lived species

Bark: Gray or reddish brown, fibrous, thin, interconnecting shallow ridges, sometimes shredded, often with spiral pattern around the main trunk

Twigs: Brown, flattened and generally rough, covered in green foliage for 2 to 3 years

Leaves: Opposite or two-ranked; scalelike, small, 1/8 inches long, overlapping and arranged in flattened branchlets or sprays, bright green above and pale green below, aromatic fragrance when crushed

Flowers: Monoecious; male cones wither quickly after pollen dispersal, female cones persistent

Fruit: Woody cone; ellipsoid, up to ½ inch long, borne upright, singly or in clusters, light brown, 6 to 12 scales, small spine on tip, often persistent on the tree

Wood: Lightweight, fragrant, durable, heartwood highly resistant to decay, whitish brown

Uses: Limited commercial value in Illinois; lumber, fencing, posts, decking, outdoor furniture, siding, cabin logs, shingles, decoys, novelties, wood turning, and pulp-wood; commonly planted as an ornamental and for windbreaks

Habitat: This uncommon, although native, Illinois species occurs naturally along select limestone and sandstone outcrops. It is commonly found growing in uplands, forested riparian areas, bogs, fens, and swamps as this species moves north and east along its natural geographic range.

Range: Native to Illinois; southwest extent is north-central and northeast Illinois; more common to the Lake States of Michigan, Minnesota, and Wisconsin; moving north and east to Ontario, Quebec, New Brunswick, New York, Vermont, New Hampshire, and Maine; gradually moving south down the Appalachian Mountains to North Carolina and Tennessee

Distinguishing features: Northern white-cedar is distinguished by the strong, flattened appearance of scalelike leaves and branchlets; thin, fibrous, shredded, and sometimes spiraling gray or reddish brown bark; and aromatic foliage.

Northern White-Cedar

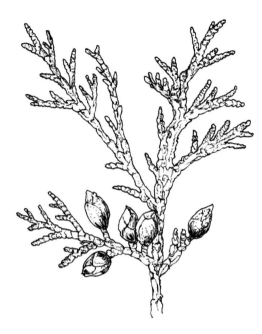

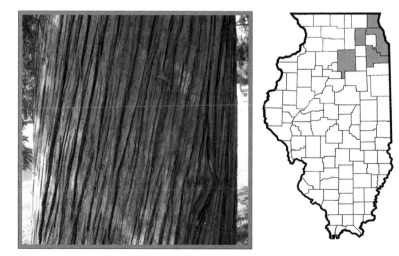

AMERICAN BASSWOOD
Tilia americana L.

Other names: Linden

Growth form: Large tree, up to 100 feet tall; trunk diameter up to 3 feet; crown broadly rounded

Bark: Gray to brown, scaly, narrowly furrowed

Twigs: Slender, gray or brown, smooth; leaf scars alternate, half-elliptical, with multiple bundle traces

Buds: Ovoid, red, smooth, up to $1/4$ inch long

Leaves: Alternate, simple; blades ovate, pointed at the tip, heart-shaped at the very asymmetrical base, up to 8 inches long, up to two-thirds as broad, coarsely toothed along the edges, green and smooth on the upper surface, paler and smooth or with tufts of hair on the undersurface; petioles up to 2 inches long, smooth

Flowers: Perfect; few in clusters on a long stalk attached to a paddle-shaped structure, each flower fragrant, greenish yellow, with 5 petals, appearing in June and July

Fruit: Nutlet; hard, spherical but often with a short point at the tip, up to $1/3$ inch in diameter, light brown, finely hairy; attached to leaflike bract

Wood: Diffuse-porous; lightweight, close-grained, pale to reddish brown

Uses: A valuable timber species; high-quality lumber, veneer, furniture, pulpwood, doors, paneling, interior finishing, novelties, food containers, boxes, crates, blocking, pallets, and firewood

Habitat: Well-drained to moderately well-drained upland forests; prefers rich, deep, moist, upland sites, including coves, low slopes, and ravines; also found on terraced bottomland forest sites with excellent drainage

Range: Native to Illinois; New Brunswick across to Manitoba, south to Texas, east to North Carolina

Distinguishing features: The large, heart-shaped leaves sometimes resemble the leaves of red mulberry, but the petioles of American basswood do not contain milky sap. American basswood differs from white basswood by the virtual absence of hairs on the undersurface of the leaves.

American Basswood

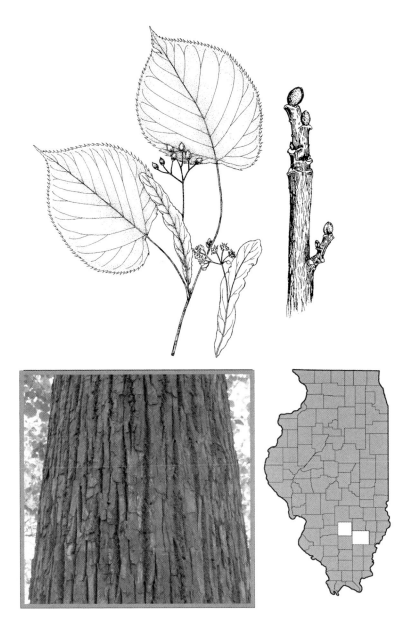

WHITE BASSWOOD

Tilia americana var. *heterophylla* (Vent.) Loud.

Growth form: Medium-sized, up to 70 feet tall; trunk diameter up to 2 feet; crown broadly spreading

Bark: Brown, scaly, moderately furrowed

Twigs: Slender, pale red–brown, smooth; leaf scars alternate, half-elliptical, with 3 to several bundle traces

Buds: Ovoid, red, usually smooth, up to $1/4$ inch long

Leaves: Alternate, simple; blades ovate, pointed at the tip, heart-shaped at the asymmetrical base, up to 6 inches long, about one-half as wide, coarsely toothed along the edges, green and somewhat smooth on the upper surface, densely covered with white hairs on the undersurface; petioles up to 2 inches long, more or less smooth

Flowers: Perfect; several in clusters on a long stalk attached to a paddle-shaped structure, each flower fragrant, greenish yellow, hairy, with 5 petals, appearing in June and July

Fruit: Nutlet; hard, more or less spherical, somewhat pointed at the tip, up to $1/3$ inch in diameter, reddish brown, finely hairy; attached to leaflike bract

Wood: Diffuse-porous; lightweight, close-grained, pale to reddish brown

Uses: Limited commercial value in Illinois; high-quality lumber, veneer, furniture, pulpwood, doors, paneling, interior finishing, novelties, food containers, boxes, crates, blocking, pallets, and firewood

Habitat: Well-drained to moderately well-drained upland forests; prefers rich, deep, moist upland sites, including coves, low slopes, and ravines

Range: Native to Illinois; New York across to Missouri, south to Mississippi and Georgia

Distinguishing features: The dense coat of white hairs on the undersurface of the leaves distinguishes white basswood from American basswood.

White Basswood

POISON SUMAC
Toxicodendron vernix (L.) Kuntze

Growth form: Small tree or shrub, up to 20 feet tall; trunk diameter up to 5 inches; crown narrowly rounded

Bark: Gray, smooth

Twigs: Rather stout, smooth, orange–brown to gray; leaf scars alternate, rounded except for where the bud is, with several bundle traces

Buds: Rounded or somewhat pointed, about $1/4$ inch in diameter, except for the larger, terminal one, hairy, often purplish

Leaves: Alternate, pinnately compound, with 7 to 13 leaflets; leaflets elliptic to obovate, pointed at the tip, rounded or tapering to the base, up to 4 inches long, up to one-half as wide, dark green and smooth on the upper surface, paler and usually smooth on the undersurface, the edges without teeth; autumn color scarlet

Flowers: Polygamo-dioecious; staminate and pistillate sometimes borne on separate plants, sometimes on the same plant, sometimes in the same flower; numerous in much-branched clusters, appearing from May to July, each flower greenish yellow and small

Fruit: Drupe; cluster of white or creamy berries, each berry round, smooth, shiny, up to $1/2$ inch in diameter, containing a single yellow seed

Wood: Soft, lightweight, coarse-grained, yellow–brown

Uses: None; skin irritant

Habitat: Bogs and swampy forests

Range: Native to Illinois; Maine across southern Ontario to Minnesota, south to Texas, east to Florida

Distinguishing features: This species differs from other sumacs with numerous leaflets by the absence of teeth along the edges of the leaves and by the absence of a winged stalk between the leaflets.

Poison Sumac

WINGED ELM
Ulmus alata Michx.

Growth form: Small to medium-sized tree, up to 60 feet tall; trunk diameter up to 2 feet but usually much smaller; crown oblong and relatively narrow

Bark: Dark gray, with shallow furrows

Twigs: Slender, gray or brown; more or less zigzag, smooth, often with corky wings; leaf scars alternate, half-round, each with 3 bundle traces

Buds: Narrow, pointed, brown, smooth or slightly hairy, up to $1/4$ inch long

Leaves: Alternate, simple; blades elliptic to oblong-lanceolate, pointed at the tip, rounded at the slightly asymmetrical base, up to 3 inches long, doubly toothed along the edges, green and smooth or slightly roughened on the upper surface, paler and hairy on the undersurface; petioles short, stout, hairy

Flowers: Perfect; in drooping clusters of 2 to 7, appearing before the leaves unfold, greenish, hairy, small

Fruit: Samara; oblong, winged, up to $1/3$ inch long, hairy along the edges, each wing notched at the top and surrounding a single central seed

Wood: Ring-porous; heavy, hard, pale brown

Uses: Tool handles, wood carvings

Habitat: Upland and bottomland forests

Range: Native to Illinois; Virginia across to Missouri, south to Texas, east to Florida

Distinguishing features: The corky wings distinguish winged elm from all other Illinois elms except rock elm. It differs from rock elm by its shorter, hairy petioles and its usually smaller leaves.

Winged Elm

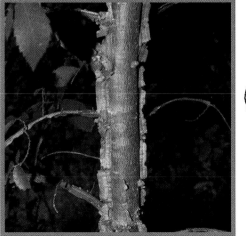

AMERICAN ELM
Ulmus americana L.

Growth form: Large tree, up to 100 feet tall; trunk diameter up to 4 feet; crown broadly rounded or sometimes flattopped, usually with drooping branchlets

Bark: Light or dark gray, furrowed, at maturity breaking into thin plates

Twigs: Brown, slender, smooth or sparsely hairy, often zigzag; leaf scars alternate, half-round, each with 3 bundle traces

Buds: Broadly ovoid, reddish brown, smooth or sparsely hairy, up to $1/4$ inch long

Leaves: Alternate, simple; blades oval to elliptic, pointed at the tip, strongly asymmetrical at the base, up to 6 inches long and about one-half as wide, coarsely doubly toothed along the edges, the upper surface dark green and smooth, the undersurface pale and either softly hairy or smooth; petioles very short, usually yellow

Flowers: Perfect; in drooping clusters of 3 or 4, appearing before the leaves unfold, greenish red, hairy, small

Fruit: Samara; oval, winged fruits up to $1/2$ inch long, margin hairy, each wing deeply notched at the top and surrounding a single central seed

Wood: Ring-porous; moderately heavy, strong, pale brown to reddish brown

Uses: Commercial value; lumber, face veneer, furniture, pulpwood, flooring, paneling, cabinets, containers, slack cooperage, crates, boxes, pallets, and firewood

Habitat: Moderately well-drained to somewhat poorly drained bottomland forests; by preference a bottomland species; occupies marginal to rich upland forest sites

Range: Native to Illinois; Nova Scotia across to southern Manitoba, south to central Texas, east to south-central Florida

Distinguishing features: American elm may be distinguished from winged elm and rock elm by its lack of corky wings on the branchlets. It differs from slippery elm by its relatively smooth leaves and the lack of rusty-colored hairs on its buds. Siberian elm, which also is similar, does not have distinctly asymmetrical leaves. Hackberry leaves, which are also somewhat similar in appearance, have three main veins originating at the base of each leaf.

American Elm

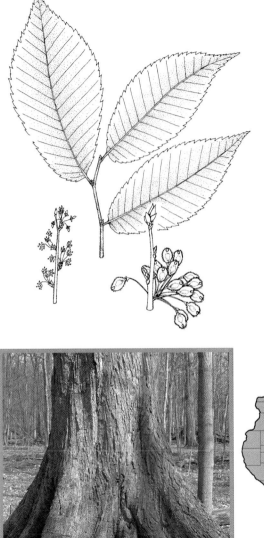

SIBERIAN ELM
Ulmus pumila L.

Growth form: Medium-sized tree, up to 70 feet tall; trunk diameter up to 2 feet; crown broadly rounded, with slender branchlets

Bark: Gray or brown, shallowly furrowed at maturity

Twigs: Slender, brown or grayish, smooth; leaf scars alternate, half-round, with 3 bundle traces

Buds: Spherical, reddish brown, up to $1/8$ inch in diameter, somewhat hairy

Leaves: Alternate, simple; blades short-pointed at the tip, tapering or rounded at the asymmetrical base, up to 3 inches long, up to one-half as broad, mostly singly toothed along the edges, smooth on both surfaces; petioles very short, usually smooth

Flowers: Perfect; in drooping clusters of 2 to 5, appearing before the leaves begin to unfold, greenish, small, without petals

Fruit: Samara; nearly round, winged fruits, up to $1/2$ inch in diameter, not notched, smooth, 1-seeded

Wood: Ring-porous; hard, heavy, pale brown

Uses: Planted as an ornamental

Habitat: Along roads, frequently reproducing around buildings

Range: Introduced from Asia; naturalized throughout Illinois, widely planted across the central and eastern United States

Distinguishing features: Siberian Elm is distinguished by its small, smooth, singly toothed leaves.

Siberian Elm

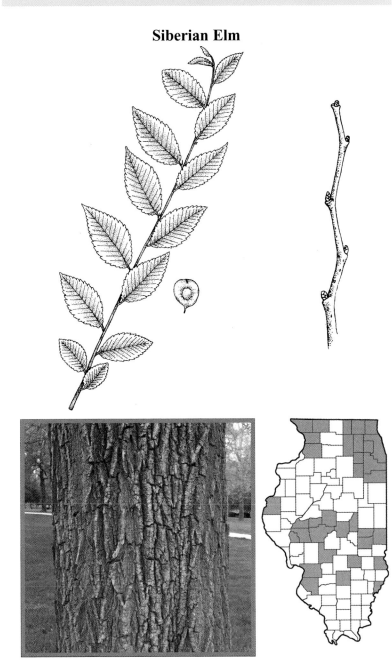

SLIPPERY ELM
Ulmus rubra Muhl.

Other names: Red elm

Growth form: Medium-sized to large tree, up to 80 feet tall; trunk diameter up to 4 feet; crown broadly rounded or occasionally flattopped

Bark: Reddish brown to gray, with shallow furrows

Twigs: Rather stout, reddish brown, with short, gray hairs; leaf scars alternate, half-round, each with 3 bundle traces

Buds: Nearly round, up to $1/4$ inch in diameter, with rusty-colored hairs

Leaves: Alternate, simple; blades oval to elliptic, pointed at the tip, strongly asymmetrical at the base, up to 7 inches long, about one-half as wide, coarsely doubly toothed along the edges, upper surface green and very rough to the touch, undersurface smooth or hairy; petioles stout, hairy, up to $1/2$ inch long

Flowers: Perfect; in drooping clusters, appearing before the leaves unfold, greenish, hairy, small

Fruit: Samara; circular, winged fruits up to $3/4$ inch in diameter, margin smooth, each wing surrounding a single seed

Wood: Ring-porous; moderately heavy, strong, pale brown to redish brown

Uses: Commercial value; lumber, face veneer, furniture, pulpwood, rough flooring, paneling, cabinets, containers, slack cooperage, crates, boxes, pallets, blocking, and firewood

Habitat: A classic generalist; thrives in well-drained bottomland and upland forests

Range: Native to Illinois; Quebec across Ontario to North Dakota, south to Texas, east to Florida

Distinguishing features: The rough, sandpapery texture of the asymmetrical leaves distinguishes this elm from all others in the state.

Slippery Elm

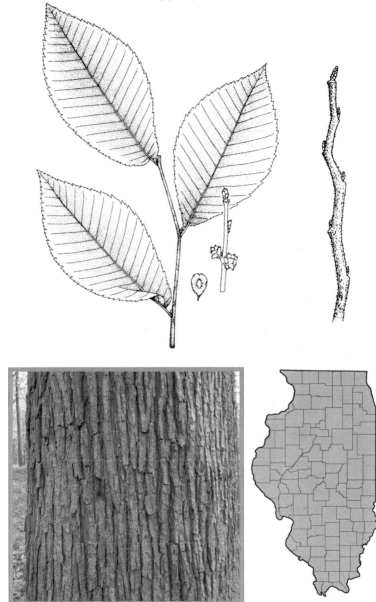

ROCK ELM
Ulmus thomasii Sarg.

Other names: Cork elm

Growth form: Medium-sized tree, up to 75 feet tall; trunk diameter up to 3 feet; crown narrow, oblong, with drooping branches

Bark: Grayish brown, with shallow furrows

Twigs: Slender, brown, smooth or finely hairy, usually with corky wings; leaf scars alternate, half-round, each with 3 bundle traces

Buds: Lance-shaped, pointed, brown, more or less hairy, up to $1/4$ inch long

Leaves: Alternate, simple; blades oval to oblong, pointed at the tip, rounded at the slightly asymmetrical base, up to 4 inches long, doubly toothed, green, smooth, and shiny on the upper surface, paler and hairy on the undersurface; petioles up to $1/2$ inch long, smooth

Flowers: Perfect; in drooping clusters of 2 to 4, appearing before the leaves begin to unfold, greenish red, hairy, small

Fruit: Samara; oval, winged fruits up to $1/2$ inch long, hairy, each wing with a shallow notch at the top and surrounding a single seed

Wood: Ring-porous; hard, strong, heavy, close-grained, pale brown to reddish brown

Uses: Limited commercial value in Illinois; lumber, veneer, furniture, pulpwood, rough flooring, baskets, cabinets, containers, slack cooperage, crates, boxes, pallets, blocking, and firewood

Habitat: Somewhat excessively drained to moderately well-drained upland forests

Range: Native to Illinois; Quebec to Ontario and Minnesota, southwestward to Kansas, east to Tennessee

Distinguishing features: Rock elm differs from other elms in Illinois by its corky-winged twigs and its smooth petioles.

Rock Elm

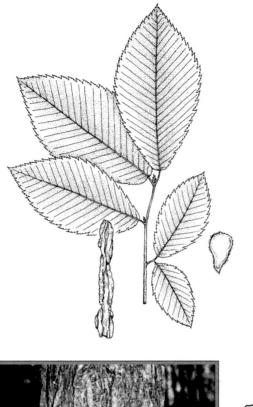

NANNYBERRY
Viburnum lentago L.

Other names: Sweet viburnum

Growth form: Small tree, up to 25 feet tall; trunk diameter up to 5 inches; crown rounded

Bark: Reddish brown, broken into irregular plates

Twigs: Slender, grayish, sometimes with orange dots, smooth; leaf scars opposite, crescent-shaped, with 3 bundle traces

Buds: Red, nearly smooth, long-pointed, up to 1 inch long

Leaves: Opposite, simple; blades ovate, pointed at the tip, tapering or rounded at the base, up to 3 inches long, about one-half as wide, sharply and finely toothed along the edges, green and slightly hairy on the upper surface, yellow–green and minutely black-dotted on the undersurface; petioles up to $1^{1}/_{2}$ inches long, sometimes rusty-hairy, typically winged

Flowers: Perfect; many in broad, round-topped clusters, slightly fragrant, appearing during April and May, each flower small and creamy white

Fruit: Drupe; fleshy, oval to ellipsoid, blue–black, up to $^{1}/_{2}$ inch long, sweet, containing a single stone

Wood: Hard, heavy, close-grained, dark orange–brown

Uses: Commonly planted for wildlife or as an ornamental

Habitat: Dry, rocky to fertile well-drained forests

Range: Native to Illinois; Quebec across to Manitoba, south to Colorado, east across northern Illinois to Georgia

Distinguishing features: Nannyberry, like other viburnums, has opposite simple leaves which are finely and sharply toothed. It differs from other viburnums in Illinois by its long, pointed leaves (some or all leaves 1 inch broad or broader) and its winged petioles.

Nannyberry

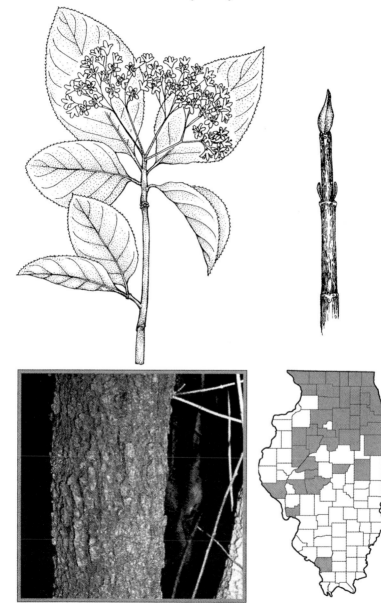

BLACKHAW
Viburnum prunifolium L.

Growth form: Small tree up to 25 feet tall; trunk diameter up to 6 inches; crown irregular

Bark: Reddish brown, broken into irregular plates

Twigs: Slender, grayish, sometimes with orange dots, smooth; leaf scars opposite, crescent-shaped, with 3 bundle traces

Buds: Brown, nearly smooth, up to $1/2$ inch long

Leaves: Opposite, simple; blades oval to ovate, short-pointed at the tip, rounded or tapering to the base, tip to 3 inches long and 2 inches broad, finely and sharply toothed along the edges, dark green and smooth on the upper surface, paler and smooth on the undersurface; petioles up to $3/4$ inch long, smooth, scarcely or not at all winged

Flowers: Perfect; many in broad, round-topped clusters, appearing during April and May, each flower small and white

Fruit: Drupe; fleshy, oval to ellipsoid, blue–black, up to $3/4$ inch long, sweet, containing a single stone

Wood: Hard, heavy, strong but brittle, coarse-grained, reddish brown

Uses: Commonly planted for wildlife or as an ornamental

Habitat: Dry, rocky to fertile well-drained forests

Range: Native to Illinois; Connecticut across to Michigan, southwest to Kansas, south to Texas, east to Florida

Distinguishing features: Blackhaw differs from nannyberry by the absence of wings along the petioles. It differs from the rusty blackhaw by the absence of rusty hairs on the buds and petioles.

Blackhaw

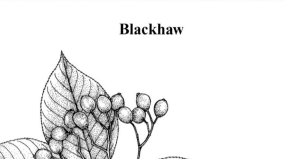

RUSTY BLACKHAW
Viburnum rufidulum Raf.

Growth form: Small tree, up to 30 feet tall; trunk diameter up to 8 inches; crown irregular

Bark: Dark brown, broken into square plates

Twigs: Slender, somewhat rusty-hairy; leaf scars opposite, crescent-shaped, with 3 bundle traces

Buds: Rusty-hairy, up to $1/2$ inch long

Leaves: Opposite, simple; blades elliptic to obovate, short-pointed or rounded at the tip, rounded or tapering to the base, up to 3 inches long, about one-half as wide, sharply and finely toothed along the edges, dark green and usually smooth on the upper surface, paler and with some rusty hairs on the undersurface; petioles up to $3/4$ inch long, rusty-hairy

Flowers: Perfect; many in broad, round-topped clusters, appearing during April and May, each flower small and creamy white

Fruit: Drupe; fleshy, oblong to obovoid, blue–black, up to $3/4$ inch long, sweet, containing a single stone

Wood: Hard, heavy, strong but brittle, close-grained, dark orange–brown

Uses: Sometimes planted as an ornamental

Habitat: Dry, rocky forests

Range: Native to Illinois; Virginia across to Missouri, south to Texas, east to Florida

Distinguishing features: The most distinguishing characteristics of the rusty blackhaw are the rusty-hairy buds and petioles.

Rusty Blackhaw

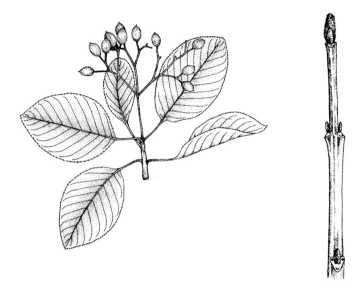

Botanical Terminology

Acorn – dry fruit, nut, typical of oak (*Quercus* spp.)

Alternate – pertains to leaf arrangement; leaves (leaf scars) are not paired directly across from each other on the twig, rather they display a staggered pattern of arrangement along the twig

Axil – angle formed by the petiole and twig

Berry – fleshy fruit; fleshy pericarp with many seeds (for example, persimmon and pawpaw)

Blade (lamina) – the flattened expanded portion of a leaf

Bract – any reduced, leaflike appendage associated with a cone, fruit, or flower

Bud – terminal, pseudoterminal, lateral (axillary) types; usually covered with one or more scales from which immature leaves, flowers, and stems develop

Bud Scale – small, protective scalelike outgrowth on the outer surface of a bud

Capsule – dry fruit with more than one section that usually opens upon maturity (for example, *Populus* spp.)

Catkin – a pendulous spike consisting of unisexual (usually) flowers

Dioecious – plant with staminate (male) flowers and pistillate (female) flowers borne separately on separate plants

Drupe – a small fleshy fruit with a hard endocarp or pit (for example, hackberry, black cherry, and dogwood); multiple of drupelets (for example, mulberry)

Fissured – netlike channels caused by splitting (growth) of the bark

Furrowed – bark pattern with long, narrow ridges and grooves/furrows

Glabrous – smooth surface without hairs

Glaucous – surface with a white or bluish powdery cast that is removable by touch

Globose – spherical in shape

Hardwoods – general term used to classify flowering broadleaf (usually deciduous) tree species (angiosperms: oak, hickory, maple, ash, elm, etc.); does not necessarily correlate with wood specific gravity

Imperfect – refers to flower structure; flower lacks either staminate or pistillate reproductive structures (for example hickory, oak, and walnut)

Legume – a podlike fruit structure common to trees in the family Fabaceae (for example, redbud, Kentucky coffeetree, honeylocust, and yellowwood)

Lenticel – small, lens-shaped pores on some twigs that allow for air–gas exchange

Lobe – rounded segment of the leaf margin

Margin – edge or perimeter of a leaf or leaflet

Midvein (midrib) – main or central rib/vein of a leaf

Monoecious – plant with staminate (male) flowers and pistillate (female) flowers borne separately on the same plant

Nut – one-seeded dry fruit with a hard wall, often enclosed or partially so in a husk or cap (for example, beech, oak, walnut, and hickory)

Opposite – pertains to leaf arrangement; leaves (leaf scars) are paired directly across from each other on the twig

Ovoid – oval or egg-shaped

Perfect – refers to flower structure; flower contains both staminate and pistillate reproductive structures (Ex: blue ash, dogwood, and basswood)

Petiole – short or long stalk that attaches the leaf, compound or simple, to the twig; usually swollen at the base

Petiolule – short or long stalk that attaches a leaflet to the rachis/rachilla on compound leaves

Pith – central portion of a twig; solid (continuous), diaphragmed, or chambered

Polygamo-dioecious – a plant with staminate (male) flowers and pistillate (female) flowers borne separately on separate plants, but this plant also contains a percentage of perfect flowers (for example, honeylocust, blackgum, and water tupelo).

Polygamo-monoecious – a plant with staminate (male) flowers and pistillate (female) flowers borne separately on the same plant, but this plant also contains a percentage of perfect flowers (for example, buckeye, hackberry, and sugarberry).

Polygamous – both perfect and imperfect flowers occur on the same plant

Pome – a small fruit that resembles an apple (for example, crabapple, serviceberry, and hawthorn)

Rachilla – secondary stem structure (axis) where leaflets attach on a bipinnately compound leaf; essentially a second-order rachis

Rachis – main stem structure (axis) where leaflets attach on a pinnately compound leaf; petioles are located at the base of the rachis on pinnately and bipinnately compound leaves

Samara – generally flat, single- or double-winglike fruit structure (for example, ash, maple, and elm)

Sessile – attached to the base directly with no visible stalk

Scale – thin, greatly reduced leaf or outgrowth

Sinus – indentation or space between lobes on the margin of a leaf

Softwoods – general term used to classify tree species that produce woody cones, that is, conifers (gymnosperms: spruce, pine, fir, cedar, cypress, hemlock, etc.); does not necessarily correlate with wood specific gravity

Stipule – a small, leaflike vegetative appendage at the base of a petiole

Tomentose – covered with down or matted hairs

Tree – a woody perennial plant having a central stem with a minimum diameter of 3 inches, a defined crown, and a minimum vertical height of 13 feet

Vein – vascular portion of a leaf

Whorled – pertains to leaf arrangement; leaves (leaf scars) are clustered around the twig opposite each other in a spiral pattern

ADDITIONAL RESOURCES

Illinois Department of Natural Resources
Division of Forest Resources
http://dnr.state.il.us/conservation/forestry

The Illinois General Assembly has given this division the responsibility for all activities concerning the forest and tree resources of Illinois. The division strives to fulfill its responsibilities by

- protecting forest resources against detrimental and management factors such as wildfire, insects and diseases, invasive and exotic plants, fragmentation and parcelization of forested tracts, improper harvesting practices, harmful livestock grazing, and tree topping
- increasing public awareness of the importance of this resource to the state's health and economy
- motivating and providing technical assistande to forest landowners and urban and community leaders for the proper management of their forest resources
- implementing scientific forest management practices on department lands

The goal of this division is to promote the establishment, enhancement, management and use of Illinois's forests for multiple benefits. The division cooperates with federal, state, local, and private partners to achieve division objectives for the benefit of the forest resources in Illinois. Formal cooperative agreements exist with the United States Forest Service, USDA, Natural Resource Conservation Service, Illinois Soil and Water Conservation Districts, universities, USDA Farm Service Agency, and other organizations interested in promoting forestry in Illinois.

The Morton Arboretum
www.mortonarb.org

A good place to learn about the trees of Illinois firsthand is at the Morton Arboretum in Lisle, 25 miles west of Chicago. This privately endowed educational and scientific institution is devoted to the collection of trees, shrubs, and other plants from around the world for people to study and enjoy and to encourage their planting to enhance our environment.

On the arboretum's 1,700 acres, one can find vast collections of oaks, maples, elms, ashes, lindens, junipers, and pines, among many other families of plants, as well as geographic groupings of plants from countries throughout north temperate regions of the world. The arboretum's naturalistic, prairie-style landscape design effectively incorporates the plant collections into the rolling glacial topography.

Fourteen miles of trails ramble through these plant collections and the arboretum's 900 acres of natural areas, which showcase marvelous examples of oak–maple woodlands and the inspiring 100-acre Schulenberg Prairie and savanna. The Big Rock Visitor Station and Prairie Visitor Station provide interpretive trailheads introducing visitors to topics of ecological, geological, and historical interest in these areas. There also are interpretive panels along many of the trails. Collections and natural areas are especially spectacular in spring, with flowering trees and wildflowers, and during autumn color.

University of Illinois at Urbana–Champaign, Department of Natural Resources and Environmental Sciences
www.nres.uiuc.edu

The department has programs in instruction, research, and public service in forest science and related natural resources fields. The instructional program offers professional undergraduate instruction in forest science and is accredited by the Society of American Foresters. Our students are broadly trained in many aspects of forest ecology and management, including forest ecology, soils, wildlife, biometrics, silviculture, geographic information systems, hydrology, and how humans interact with various ecosystems. Graduate training is provided at the masters and doctoral levels and allows students to customize their program for any aspect of environmental or natural resource management.

Research is conducted throughout the nation and the world but is locally focused at the main campus, the Dixon Springs Agricultural Center in southern Illinois (Pope County), and at other smaller, outlying university research sites. Support is provided by the Illinois Agricultural Experiment Station and grants from industry and government. Projects cover a wide range of subjects related to the production and utilization of wood, as well as the use of forests for non-timber values. The latter includes recreation, and wildlife and watershed management, with special emphasis on the role of forests and forestry in water quality and carbon sequestration.

University of Illinois Arboretum
http://arboretum.illinois.edu/

In 1990, the University of Illinois approved a 160-acre arboretum site bounded by Florida Avenue on the north, Lincoln Avenue on the west, Windsor Road on the south, and Orchard Downs on the east. The first major addition to the Arboretum was the Miles C. Hartley Garden, completed in 1994. Since that time, new additions include the Noel Welcome Garden (1996), Japan House (1998), and ponds (1998) adjacent to Japan House. Design and implementation of the gardens surrounding Japan House were undertaken the same year. These gardens are the more formal elements of the Arboretum, which also has a selection of trees commonly found in Illinois forests and landscapes.

The University of Illinois Arboretum provides an ideal setting for a leisurely walk through its gardens, open fields, and canopy of trees. A walking trail highlighting 30 trees was developed by Dr. David Williams, professor of horticulture, with assistance from Keith Irwin and Beth Smith, graduate students in the Departments of Landscape Architecture and Natural Resources and Environmental Sciences, respectively. A brochure for those wishing a self-guiding tour provides information concerning landscape value, points of interest about the trees, and their native range. It contains a map providing a numerical guide that corresponds to the sequence of trees presented in the text and can be downloaded from the Arboretum's Web site.

The newest plans for the Arboretum include development of the Heritage Garden. Showcasing the unique contributions of Illinois's woody-, perennial-, and annual-plant breeders in a beautiful and educational setting, the new Heritage Garden will exemplify the University's preeminent status within the developing global "green industry." The garden will provide a fitting gateway to the Arboretum and a setting for transformative learning experiences in the plant sciences, the arts, and landscape design—while simultaneously serving as a welcoming focal point for visitors to the University.

University of Illinois Extension Forestry
http://web.extension.uiuc.edu/forestry

University of Illinois Extension Forestry is the gateway to reliable and scientifically sound assistance and solutions concerning forest-management issues, activities, and objectives. It is our mission to promote and provide forestry education and outreach to Illinois citizens, with special emphasis directed at Illinois's 170,000 forest landowners who own and control over 82% of the state's forest resources. Please visit our Web site to learn more about forest management, reforestation, professional forestry assistance, timber harvesting, timber prices, agroforestry, and state and federal forestry-assistance programs.

Southern Illinois University–Carbondale
www.siuc.edu

Southern Illinois University–Carbondale has both a Department of Plant Biology and a Department of Forestry where students may select courses from a broad curriculum to study various aspects of plants and forest life. Many forest-oriented courses are available, and most of them include actual work in the field. The university has a greenhouse facility on campus where collections of native and exotic species are maintained. Guided tours of this display greenhouse can be arranged by contacting the chair of the Department of Plant Biology, Southern Illinois University, Carbondale, Illinois 62901-6509.

Shawnee National Forest
www.fs.fed.us/r9/forests/shawnee

Much of the forested land in the southern tip of Illinois is in the Shawnee National Forest. The 290,000 acres of rolling topography in the forest contain 208 different kinds of native woody plants. Some of the areas that have a high concentration of plant life have been designated as Natural Areas by the United States Forest Service. At these areas, such as Bell Smith Springs, Little Grand Canyon, Jackson Hollow, LaRue-Pine Hills, Stone Face, and 75 others, plant life is protected. These are excellent places to observe many of the woody plants of the state.

At other areas in the Shawnee National Forest, various forest-management practices, such as prescribed burning, timber harvesting, and watershed protection, can be observed. Numerous recreation facilities are dotted throughout the Shawnee. At many of these, nature trails have been developed that bring the hiker closer to nature. Descriptive brochures are available for most of the recreation areas.

Illinois Forestry Development Council
http://ifdc.nres.uiuc.edu

The Illinois Forestry Development Council, created by passage of the Illinois Forestry Development Act of 1983, is charged to study and evaluate the forest resources and forest industry of Illinois. The council determines the magnitude, nature, extent, and ownership of Illinois's forest resources, and the uses, benefits, and services these resources provide. The council also evaluates economic development, employment, and management opportunities related to the forest industry. They consider staffing and funding needs for forestry programs, education needs, as well as the soil, water and wildlife habitat benefits that forestry practices offer.

The council provides a comprehensive framework to maintain and enhance forest resources of Illinois so they can be enjoyed by Illinois's citizens for years to come. The council also encourages cooperation among all concerned parties to work toward enhancement of our many forest communities. Twenty-four members serve on the council, representing all aspects of forestry in Illinois.

State Tree of Illinois

In 1972, the school children of Illinois selected the white oak (*Quercus alba*) as the state tree. It is truly representative for it can be found throughout the state on a variety of sites. Growing to its largest size on upland, cool, well-drained coves, slopes, and terraces, it often reaches 100 feet in height and 3 feet in diameter.

White oak is one of Illinois's most valuable trees. It makes an excellent shade tree of majestic beauty with a broad, round head and wide, spreading branches. Commercially, it is an extremely valuable species used for lumber, veneer, wine and whiskey barrels, furniture, flooring, and cabinets.

This species also is a part of our national heritage. In the War of 1812, sailors reported that during battle, cannon balls bounced off the white oak hull of the U.S.S. Constitution, helping make her "Old Ironsides" a part of our history.

Illinois Big Tree Register
http://web.extension.uiuc.edu/forestry

The Illinois Big Tree Register is more than just the relentless pursuit of the largest native trees in the state. It is a forestry and natural resources awareness campaign to bring trees, nature, and people together in a fun, interactive, exciting, and competitive arena. Inspired by American Forests' National Register of Big Trees, the Illinois Department of Natural Resources initiated the Illinois Big Tree Register in 1962. In 2006, the administration and maintenance of the Illinois Big Tree Register was transferred to the University of Illinois. A complete list of native champion trees, including information on how to nominate and measure a potential champion tree, can be viewed on the University of Illinois Extension Forestry's Web site.

Illinois Forestry Association
www.ilforestry.org

Established in 2006, the Illinois Forestry Association is a 501(c)3 grass-roots organization with the mission to "act on issues that impact rural and community forests and to promote forestry throughout the state." The Illinois Forestry Association has over 700 active members committed to bringing forestry-related issues to the attention of state legislators, local government, natural resources organizations, citizen groups, and the general public. Whether you are a homeowner, landowner, student, teacher, forester, natural resource manager, logger, or concerned citizen, the Illinois Forestry Association is dedicated to address your issues related to forestry and natural resources. Membership is open to everyone ... join today!

Illinois Tree Farm
www.IllinoisTreeFarm.org

The Illinois Tree Farm serves the entire state of Illinois—focusing on managing Illinois private forest lands for timber production, nontimber forest products, and ecosystem services. As part of the American Tree Farm System, the Illinois Tree Farm proudly boasts over 1,070 certified tree farms, totaling nearly 93,000 acres. This unique organization is a great way to interact with other tree farmers and forestry professionals; learn about new forest-management techniques by attending local Tree Farm field days; and learn about new state and federal forestry programs, including timber taxation, wood certification, and carbon sequestration. Visit our Web site to learn more about the Illinois Tree Farm and what the nation's oldest and most prestigious private-forest landowner organization can do for you!

The Illinois Steward Magazine
http://ilsteward.extension.uiuc.edu

The Illinois Steward magazine is a quarterly publication of University of Illinois Extension and its partners that promotes natural resource stewardship. Articles cover wide-ranging topics, including some directly related to managing forest resources. Other articles foster respect and awareness of woodland ecosystems that sustain our emotional well-being. All articles help us discover our place in the natural world.

To preview the stellar photographs, striking graphic design, and engaging articles that have earned numerous national awards for *The Illinois Steward,* please visit the magazine's Web site to review the article topics in past issues, as well as sample articles. Subscription information and rates are also given. If you enjoy the natural world and want to become a better steward of our natural resources, consider subscribing to *The Illinois Steward* magazine.

Index to Common and Scientific Names

Acer
  barbatum, 42
  negundo, 44
  nigrum, 46
  rubrum, 48
    var. *drummondii*, 50
  saccharinum, 52
  saccharum, 54

Aesculus
  flava, 56
  glabra, 58
  pavia, 60

Ailanthus
  altissima, 62

Alder
  European, 64

Alnus
  glutinosa, 64

Amelanchier
  arborea, 66
  laevis, 68

Aralia
  spinosa, 70

Ash
  Black, 144
  Blue, 150
  Green, 146
  Pumpkin, 148
  White, 142

Asimina
  triloba, 72

Aspen
  Bigtooth, 222
  Quaking, 226

Baldcypress, 300

Basswood
  American, 304
  White, 306

Beech
  American, 136

Betula
  alleghaniensis, 74
  nigra, 76
  papyrifera, 78

Birch
  Paper, 78
  River, 76
  Yellow, 72

Blackhaw, 322
  Rusty, 324

Black Cherry, 234

Blackgum, 194

Boxelder, 44

Broussonetia
  papyrifera, 80

Buckeye
  Ohio, 58
  Red, 60
  Yellow, 56

Buckthorn
  Carolina, 140
  Common, 280

Butternut, 164

Carpinus
  caroliniana, 82

Carya
  alba, 84
  aquatica, 86
  cordiformis, 88
  glabra, 90
  illinoinensis, 92
  laciniosa, 94
  ovalis, 96
  ovata, 98
  texana, 100

Castanea
  dentata, 102

Catalpa
  bignonioides, 104
  Northern, 106
  Southern 104
  speciosa, 106

Celtis
  laevigata, 108
  occidentalis, 110
  tenuifolia, 112

Cercis
  canadensis, 114

Cherry
  Black, 234

Chestnut
    American, 102

Chokecherry, 236

Cladrastis
    kentukea, 116

Coffeetree
    Kentucky, 156

Cornus
    alternifolia, 118
    amomum, 124
    drummondii, 120
    florida, 122
    foemina, 124
    obliqua, 124
    racemosa, 124
    rugosa, 124
    sericea, 124

Cottonwood
    Eastern, 220
    Swamp, 224

Crabapple
    Prairie, 186
    Southern, 182
    Sweet, 184

Crataegus
    calpodendron, 132
    coccinioides, 132
    crus-galli, 126
    mollis, 128
    pruinosa, 130
    punctata, 132
    viridis, 132

Cucumbertree, 180

Devils-walkingstick, 70

Diospyros
    virginiana, 134

Dogwood
    Alternate-leaf, 118
    Flowering, 122
    Gray, 124
    Red Osier, 124
    Roughleaf, 120
    Roundleaf, 124
    Silky, 124
    Stiff, 124
    Willow, 124

Elm
    American, 312
    Rock, 318
    Siberian, 314
    Slippery, 316
    Winged, 310

Fagus
    grandifolia, 136

Forestiera
    acuminata, 138

Frangula
    caroliniana, 140

Fraxinus
    americana, 142
    nigra, 144
    pennsylvanica, 146
    profunda, 148
    quadrangulata, 150

Gleditsia
    aquatica, 152
    triacanthos, 154

Gum
    Tupelo, 190

Gymnocladus
    dioicus, 156

Hackberry, 110
    Georgia, 112

Halesia
    tetraptera, 158

Hamamelis
    virginiana, 160

Hawthorn
    Cockspur, 126
    Dotted, 132
    Green, 132
    Frosted, 130
    Red, 128
    Kansas, 132
    Pear, 132

Hickory
    Bitternut, 88
    Black, 100
    Mockernut, 84
    Pecan, 92
    Pignut, 90
    Red, 96
    Shagbark, 98
    Shellbark, 94
    Water, 86

Honeylocust, 154

Hophornbeam
    Eastern, 196

Hoptree
    Common, 238

Hornbeam
    American, 82

Ilex
    decidua, 162

Juglans
    cinerea, 164
    nigra, 166

Juniperus
  virginiana, 168

Larch
  Eastern, 172
  European, 170

Larix
  decidua, 170
  laricina, 172

Liquidambar
  styraciflua, 174

Liriodendron
  tulipifera, 176

Locust
  Black, 288

Maclura
  pomifera, 178

Magnolia
  acuminata, 180

Malus
  angustifolia, 182
  coronaria, 184
  ioensis, 186

Maple
  Black, 46
  Drummond, 50
  Red, 48
  Silver, 52
  Florida, 42
  Sugar, 54

Morus
  alba, 188
  rubra, 190

Mulberry
  Paper, 80
  Red, 190
  White, 188

Nannyberry, 320

Nyssa
  aquatica, 192
  sylvatica, 194

Oak
  Black, 278
  Blackjack, 256
  Bur, 254
  Cherrybark, 262
  Chestnut, 268
  Chinkapin, 260
  Northern Pin, 246
  Northern Red, 270
  Nuttall, 276
  Overcup, 252
  Pin, 264
  Post, 274
  Scarlet, 244
  Shingle, 250
  Shumard, 272
  Southern Red, 248
  Swamp Chestnut, 258
  Swamp White, 242
  White, 240
  Willow, 266

Osage-Orange, 178

Ostrya
  virginiana, 196

Paulownia
  Royal, 198
  tomentosa, 198

Pawpaw, 72

Pecan, 92

Persimmon
  Common, 134

Pine
  Jack, 200
  Loblolly, 210
  Red, 204
  Scotch, 208
  Shortleaf, 202
  White, 206

Pinus
  banksiana, 200
  echinata, 202
  resinosa, 204
  strobus, 206
  sylvestris, 208
  taeda, 210

Planera
  aquatica, 212

Platanus
  occidentalis, 214

Plum
  American, 228
  Wildgoose, 232
  Chickasaw, 232
  Hortulan, 230

Poplar
  Balsam, 218
  White, 216

Populus
  alba, 216
  balsamifera, 218
  deltoides, 220
  grandidentata, 222
  heterophylla, 224
  tremuloides, 226

Possumhaw, 162

Prunus
    americana, 228
    angustifolia, 232
    hortulana, 230
    munsoniana, 232
    serotina, 234
    virginiana, 236

Ptelea
    trifoliata, 238

Quercus
    alba, 240
    bicolor, 242
    coccinea, 244
    ellipsoidalis, 246
    falcata, 248
    imbricaria, 250
    lyrata, 252
    macrocarpa, 254
    marilandica, 256
    michauxii, 258
    muehlenbergii, 260
    pagoda, 262
    palustris, 264
    phellos, 266
    prinus, 268
    rubra, 270
    shumardii, 272
    stellata, 274
    texana, 276
    velutina, 278

Redbud
    Eastern, 114

Redcedar
    Eastern, 168

Rhamnus
    cathartica, 280

Rhus
    copallina, 282
    glabra, 284
    hirta, 286

Robinia
    pseudoacacia, 288

Salix
    amygdaloides, 290
    caroliniana, 292
    exigua, 294
    nigra, 296

Sassafras
    albidum, 298

Serviceberry
    Allegheny, 68
    Downy, 66

Silverbell
    Carolina, 158

Sugarberry, 108

Sumac
    Poison, 308
    Shining, 282
    Smooth, 284
    Staghorn, 286

Swamp-privet, 138

Sweetgum, 174

Sycamore, 214

Tamarack, 172

Taxodium
    distichum, 300

Thuja
    occidentalis, 302

Tilia
    americana, 304
    var. *heterophylla*, 306

Toxicodendron
    vernix, 308

Tree-of-Heaven, 62

Ulmus
    alata, 310
    americana, 312
    pumila, 314
    rubra, 316
    thomasii, 318

Viburnum
    lentago, 320
    prunifolium, 322
    rufidulum, 324

Walnut, Black, 166

Water-Elm, 212

Water Tupelo, 192

Waterlocust, 152

Willow
    Black, 296
    Coastal Plain, 292
    Peachleaf, 290
    Sandbar, 294

White-Cedar
    Northern, 302

Witchhazel, 160

Yellow-Poplar, 176

Yellowwood, 116

Illustration Credits

All photographs are by John A. Richardson and Robert H. Mohlenbrock except Adam A. Agosta, School of Renewable Natural Resources, Louisiana State University Agricultural Center, 277; Steven J. Baskauf, http://bioimages.vanderbilt.edu, 323; John M. Edgington, University of Illinois, 51, 103, 199, 267; Christopher Evans, River to River CWMA, 87, 193, 211, 311; Jay C. Hayek, 45, 49, 53, 55, 57, 59, 61, 63, 65, 67, 71, 73, 75, 77, 79, 83, 85, 89, 91, 93, 95, 97, 99, 105, 107, 109, 111, 115, 117, 119, 121, 123, 135, 137, 143, 145, 147, 149, 151, 155, 157, 159, 161, 165, 167, 169, 171, 173, 175, 177, 179, 181, 189, 191, 195, 197, 201, 203, 205, 207, 209, 215, 219, 221, 223, 227, 229, 235, 237, 239, 241, 243, 245, 247, 249, 251, 253, 255, 257, 259, 261, 263, 265, 269, 271, 273, 275, 279, 285, 289, 297, 299, 301, 303, 305, 313, 315, 317; Keith Kanoti, Maine Forest Service, 309; Theresa Kissane, University of Illinois, 307; Morton Arboretum, 219.

All illustrations are by Miriam Wysong and Fredda J. Burton, Southern Illinois University, except Cindy Lamb Basham, 7, 8, 9; Clint Patterson, Illinois Department of Natural Resources, 41, 57 (fruit/leaf/twig), 219 (leaf/twig), 241 (leaf/acron), 253 (acorn), and 277 (leaf/acorn/twig).

Shop online for publications and more
from University of Illinois experts at

pubsplus.uiuc.edu